THE BOOK OF
SOLO GAMES

Dedicated to my favourite opponent – myself.

THE BOOK OF SOLO GAMES

GYLES BRANDRETH

PERENNIAL LIBRARY

Harper & Row, Publishers
New York, Cambridge, Philadelphia, San Francisco
London, Mexico City, São Paulo, Singapore, Sydney

A hardcover edition of this work was published by J. M. Dent & Sons Ltd. in Great Britain and by Peter Bedrick Books in the United States. It is reprinted by arrangement with Peter Bedrick Books.

First PERENNIAL LIBRARY edition published 1985.

Library of Congress Cataloging in Publication Data

Brandreth, Gyles Daubeney, 1948–
    The book of solo games.

    Reprint. Originally published: 1st American ed. New York : P. Bedrick Books, 1984, c1983.
    Includes index.
    1. Indoor games. 2. Games. I. Title.
GV1229.B66 1985   794   85-42555
ISBN 0-06-097004-9 (pbk.)

---

85 86 87 88 89 MPC 10 9 8 7 6 5 4 3 2 1

CONTENTS

3 Domino Games

4 Fivestones and Friends

Tiddlywinks

Marbles

Dice

5 Coins and Matches

6 Shapes and Sizes

10 Children's Games

Solutions

Index

INTRODUCTION

Dipping Into Dictionaries is the name of one of my favourite solo games and I have just been playing it. I stopped when I reached page 402 of Volume X of the Oxford English Dictionary (Sole – Sz) and discovered, to my great surprise, that there's a lot more to solitaire than ever I imagined. Apparently, as well as being what I always thought it was, a solitaire can also be a recluse, a precious stone, a solitary beast of chase, a Jamaican bird and a loose neck-tie of black silk or broad ribbon worn by men in the eighteenth century.

Naturally the solitaire that really concerns me – and you – is the game which can be played by one person'. The first usage of the word with that meaning quoted in the O.E.D. comes in a letter from the novelist Horace Walpole, dated 1746. 'Has Miss Harriet found any more ways at Solitaire?' he asks, almost in an aside, not realising that this innocuous question is putting a new word on the map – or at least into the dictionary.

As you can tell, I have learnt a lot from page 402 of Volume X of the Oxford English Dictionary. (Apart from what's relevant to the matter in hand, I'm delighted to have discovered that a soliquacious solisquious soliped is an uncloven hoofed animal that follows the sun talking to itself!) Since I have learnt so much from the book I've just been reading, I very much hope that you will learn a thing or two from the book I've just been writing.

Solo Games is intended as a comprehensive compendium of indoor games of all sorts and it is a subject I have warmed to because, at least as far as games go, I have always been a bit of a loner. All my life team games have been anathema to me. Their full horror dawned on me a quarter of a century ago, when I was ten and a pupil at a boys' boarding school in Kent. Twice a week during the winter term we were expected to play football. Twice a week during the winter term I would invent colds and coughs and psychosomatic headaches to help me avoid the torture of the soccer pitch. My finest hour came one particulary wet and windy after-noon when I pretended to have a severe stomach ache. The doctor was summoned and took me seriously, so seriously in fact that within twenty-four hours I was in Canterbury General Hospital having my one-hundred-per-cent-healthy appendix removed.

At my next school, a 'progressive' establishment called Bedales in Hampshire – famous for its distinguished parents (running from Oscar Wilde to Princess Margaret) rather than the achievements of its former pupils – I might have hoped to be excused compulsory games. Not so. The nightmare continued – for years. When at last, at the age of eighteen, I was allowed to leave the school rugby field for the very last time, I went into the changing rooms, fell to my knees and thanked God that the years of team games were behind me. Indeed, so relieved and grateful was I, that I gave my Maker a solemn promise: in return for His undertaking to excuse me from team games for the rest of my life, I promised never to complain about anything else ever again. I have tried to keep my word.

I may sound somewhat fanatical – and on this subject perhaps I am – but my loathing of team games then has one advantage now: as a child, though I didn't like playing games with others, I still liked playing games, so I made it my business to discover as many games for one player as I could – and this book is the result of my solitary endeavours.

Although Walpole only started writing letters about Solitaire a little over two hundred years ago, people have certainly been playing solo games for thousands of years. Dominoes (Chapter 3) and Fivestones (Chapter 4) are definitely pre-Christian in origin and the Chinese Tangram (Chapter 6) may be too. In the book I have included games that have been around for generations – e.g. Dice, Marbles, Tiddlywinks, in Chapter 4 – as well as games that are as modern as the electronic calculator (Chapter 7) and I have taken care to feature games from all over the world, from California in the West to Canton in the Far East. The solitaire board game that is now generally known as Solitaire is French in origin, but I have included games for players on both sides of the Channel since the French and English Solitaire boards are slightly different (Chapter 2).

Where games require boards they can usually be made very easily – often simply by being drawn onto a piece of paper or card – and for most of the games that call for 'pieces', you will find that buttons or bottle-tops give as good a game as bone or carved ebony. Indeed with the games for coins and matches (Chapter 5) their charm lies in the fact that they can be played anywhere anytime so long as you have a little loose change or a box of matches to hand. And with the games in Chapter 8, all you need is a pencil and the back of an old envelope.

Inevitably pride of place has gone to Card Games (Chapter 1) because they are so popular – it is reckoned that in Western Europe 90 per cent of all households contain at least one pack of cards and there are probably over 250,000,000,000 decks in the United States – but I have also tried to include a sprinkling of the unexpected, and alongside the many cerebral games there are a number that are simply silly (especially in Chapters 9 and 10, Mental Games and Children's Games).

As organiser of the British National Scrabble Championships – I founded the contest in 1971 – and as a former European Monopoly Champion – who shame-facedly admits he came third in the World Championships in New York – I am clearly not averse to all indoor games for two or more, but I have come to the conclusion that I am really happiest when pitting my wits against the opponent I like best: myself.

This is a book for people who get on well with themselves. We all need to be or have to be alone at frequent moments in our lives – because we're ill or we've been sent to bed early, because we live alone or our partner is taking the dog for a walk round the block, because we're on our own in an airport lounge or on a train – and this book is designed to ensure that those moments are never dull. Its aim is to make patience a positive pleasure, when once it was only a virtue.

Gyles Brandreth

| CARD GAMES

When playing cards on your own, the temptation to cheat is overwhelming, but for the sake of the game – if not for the sake of your soul – do try to play these games strictly according to the rules. If you win without cheating, the sense of achievement is wonderfully rewarding. Also before playing any of the solo games in this chapter, whether using one pack or two, do make sure the cards have been shuffled thoroughly.

Only one pack of cards is needed for the games in this section up to and including Tsarina (p. 22). The rest require two packs.

Accordion

Deal the cards face upwards one at a time in a row from left to right. Any card may be moved over on top of the card to its left or the card third to its left, provided that it is of the same suit or the same rank. A pile of two or more cards can be moved in the same way, depending on the suit and rank of the top card.

The aim is to get all fifty-two cards in one pile.

Agnes

Deal out twenty-eight cards face upwards in seven overlapping rows – seven in the first row, then six, five, four, three, two, one – forming an inverted triangle.

Deal another card and place it face upwards above the triangle. This card together with the other three cards of the same rank, when they become available, form the foundations to be built up in ascending sequence according to suit. For example, on a foundation of the 7 of clubs the sequence will be 7, 8, 9, 10, J, Q, K, A, 2, 3, 4, 5, 6 of clubs.

The rest of the pack forms the stock.

The exposed card at the bottom of each column is available to be transferred to a foundation or may be built on in descending sequence of the same colour – for example, any red 10 on a red jack, any black 3 on a black 4. When a column becomes vacant, the space may be filled by any exposed card, though you are not required to fill spaces immediately.

When you have done all the building and transferring that you can, deal seven more cards, one on the bottom of each column, and continue as before.

Continue building and then dealing, until the stock is exhausted. No second deal is permitted.

Battling Knights

Set out the four jacks face up in a row in this order: heart, club, diamond, spade. These are the four knights who will do battle to see which can capture the greatest number of cards. Red jacks capture even cards, black jacks capture odd cards. (Queens count as even, kings as odd.)

Deal out four cards face up in a row. The jack of hearts has the first go, taking all the even cards from the row. His captives are placed underneath him. Any cards that are not captured are put in a discard pile.

Deal out another four cards. It's the turn of the jack of clubs, so he captures any odd cards in this batch.

Repeat until all the cards have been dealt, each knight in turn having a go at capturing. If a knight can capture none of the cards presented to him, his turn passes to the next. A knight who captures all four also receives one of the captives held by each of the other knights (if they have any). Only one deal is permitted.

The knight with the most captives at the end of the game is the winner.

Beehive

Count off ten cards from the top of the pack and place them in a pile face upwards. These cards form the reserve or 'beehive'.

To the right of the beehive deal out six cards face upwards. This is the tableau or 'garden'. The rest of the pack forms the stock.

There are no foundations in this game. All the building is done on the tableau and is according to rank only – a 9 on a 9, a jack on a jack, etc.

Go through the stock, taking three cards at a time in a packet and placing the packet face up on a single waste pile. Building on to the tableau may be done from the top card of the waste pile, the top card of the beehive, or from one part of the garden to another. Whenever you get four cards of the same rank together in the garden, discard them and fill the space with the top card from the beehive. When the beehive is exhausted, fill spaces from the top card of the waste pile.

When all the cards in the stock have been dealt, turn over the waste pile and redeal. There is no limit to the number of times you may do this.

To be successful, you must discard the whole pack in groups of four of the same rank.

Beleaguered Castle

Set out the four aces in a vertical column to form the foundations. The tableau is formed by dealing out from left to right the rest of the pack in rows of six overlapping cards on either side of each ace.

The aim is to build up each suit in ascending sequence from ace to king on the foundations.

The exposed (rightmost) card of each of the eight rows is available for play. Only one card may be moved at a time, either on to the foundations or on to the exposed card of another row in the tableau. Building in the tableau is in descending sequence regardless of suit – for example, any jack on any queen, any 10 on any jack, etc.

When a row is completely cleared the space may be filled by any available card.

La Belle Lucie

Shuffle the pack well and deal it out in 17 fans of three cards and one single card. Traditionally these 17 fans are arranged in the shape of a larger fan with the single card as its handle.

The aim is to get out the aces as foundations, and to build on them in ascending sequence from ace to king according to suit.

The exposed (rightmost) card of each fan and the single card are available for play. You may move one card at a time, either on to a foundation or on to the exposed card of another fan in downward suit sequence. When a fan is completely cleared the space remains unfilled.

When no more play is possible, you may gather up all the cards, except those on the foundations, shuffle them well and redeal them in fans of three cards each (with the odd one or two cards at the end forming a separate fan). Only two such redeals are permitted.

Bisley

Place the four aces face upwards in a row, and then deal out another nine cards in a row to the right of the aces. Then deal out the rest of the pack in another three rows of thirteen underneath the first row. All cards are dealt face upwards.

As the kings become available in the course of play they are put in a row above their corresponding aces.

The aces and kings both serve as foundations. You build up in ascending suit sequence on the aces and build down in descending suit sequence on the kings. When the two sequences meet you put them together as a completed sequence.

The bottom card of each column in the tableau is available for play, either on to a foundation or on to the bottom card of another column in the tableau.

You can build on the bottom card of any column in either upward or downward sequence within suit – for example, on the 6 of spades you could play either the 5 of spades or the 7 of spades. You may reverse the order at any time if you wish – for example, you may play the 7 of spades on to the 6 of spades, reverse the sequence from 6–7 to 7–6, and then play the 5 of spades on the 6.

When a column becomes vacant, the space is not filled.

To be successful, it is clearly important to free the kings as soon as possible to serve as foundations.

Block Eleven

Shuffle the pack well and deal out nine cards face upwards in three rows of three. If the pips on any two cards add up to eleven (for example, an ace and a 10, a 2 and a 9, a 5 and a 6), deal another card face upwards on top of each of these. Court cards don't count in making elevens, but if a jack, queen and king all appear you may deal three more cards to cover them.

Continue in this way. If at any time there are no cards adding up to eleven and no set of three court cards then you are blocked. But if you can continue until you have dealt out all the cards then you have won.

The Carpet

Deal twenty cards face upwards in four rows of five. This is the Carpet. If any aces turn up as you are forming the Carpet, lay them to one side where they will form foundations to be built up in ascending sequence from ace to king according to suit. The remaining cards form the stock.

Deal from the stock one card at a time on to a single waste pile. The foundations can be built up from the top card of the waste pile or the top card of the stock or from the Carpet. Whenever a gap occurs in the Carpet, fill it with the top card of the waste pile or, if there are no cards in the waste pile, with the top card of the stock.

You may only deal out the stock once. By the time you have finished doing this, if you are successful you will have four complete suit sequences from ace to king on the foundations and no Carpet.

Castles in Spain

Deal a row of five cards, above that a row of four, above that a row of three, and above that a row of one – all face down. Deal another two cards face down on top of each of these cards, and then deal the remaining thirteen cards face up on top of the piles. This tableau is your Spanish castle.

The aim is to remove the aces, as they become exposed, to form foundations and to build up on them ascending sequences from ace to king according to suit.

On the tableau you may move cards to form descending sequences of alternate colour (for example, red 6 on black 7). You may also move sequences of cards from one pile to another if they will fit. Face-down cards are turned over and come into play as they become exposed. When a complete pile is cleared, leaving a space, the space may be filled by any sequence or part sequence from one of the other piles.

Clock Patience

This is the ideal game for those with time on their hands!

Shuffle the pack thoroughly and deal the cards singly face downwards into thirteen piles of four cards each. The piles are set out in the form of a clock dial, a pile at the 1 o'clock position, a pile at the 2 o'clock position, and so on, with the thirteenth pile in the centre.

Turn up the top card from the centre pile and place it face-up at the bottom of the pile where it 'belongs'. For example, an ace would go to the pile in the 1 o'clock position, a 2 to the pile in the 2 o'clock position and so on. Jacks go at 11 o'clock, queens at 12 o'clock and kings go in the centre. Whichever pile it goes to, turn up the top card of that pile and transfer this card to its correct position in the same way. Carry on doing this with each card that you turn up.

The aim is to turn up all the cards and end with a completed clock dial consisting of thirteen piles of four face-up cards in the correct positions. If you turn up the fourth king before you achieve this, however, you will find you are blocked. The game only works if a king is the last card turned up.

Clubs Out

Remove from the pack all 2s, 3s, 4s, 5s and 6s, leaving a pack of thirty-two cards.

Shuffle well, then deal three cards face upwards in a row. If any of the cards is a club throw it out and deal another card to take its place. Carry on doing this until you have three non-clubs in the row.

Deal four more rows of three, all face up. Again throw out any clubs, but this time do not fill any spaces that occur as a result.

Gather the remaining cards together with the cards left in the stock, shuffle them and perform a second deal in the same manner as the first. Then repeat the whole process once more.

To be successful you must throw out all eight clubs in the three deals.

Demon (Canfield)

Deal thirteen cards face downwards to form a reserve pile, then turn it over so that only the top card is visible. Then deal four cards face upwards in a row to the right of the reserve pile. This is the tableau.

Deal another card face upwards above the first card of the tableau to form the first of four foundations. As they become available, the other three cards of the same rank as this card will be placed to form the other three foundations. The aim is to build up a complete ascending sequence by suit on each foundation. The sequence 'turns the corner' at the ace – for example, if the first foundation is the 7 of hearts, the sequence to be built up will be 7, 8, 9, 10, J, Q, K, A, 2, 3, 4, 5, 6 of hearts, and similar sequences will be built up on the other foundations.

The remainder of the pack forms the stock. Turn over the stock in batches of three cards on to a waste pile. If there are less than three cards when you come to the end of the stock they may be turned over singly. The only card in the waste pile that is available for play is the top card though, of course, when this is played the card below becomes available.

Cards may be played on to the columns of the tableau in descending sequence of alternating colour – for example, red 10 on black jack, black 9 on red 10, etc. You may transfer an entire column, provided that this sequence is maintained.

Immediately a tableau column becomes vacant, the space must be filled with the top card of the reverse pile. If there are no cards left in the reserve pile, the space in the tableau may be filled with the top card of the waste pile, though in this case you do not need to fill the space immediately.

When the end of the stock is reached, the waste pile is turned over to form a new stock which is then redealt without shuffling. This may be performed as often as required until the game is either won or blocked.

This game seldom works out.

Eight Away

Shuffle the pack thoroughly, and deal out six rows of eight cards, all face upwards. The rows should overlap so that all the cards are visible. Deal out the remaining four cards face upwards in a row below the tableau to form the start of the reserve.

All the cards in the reserve as well as the exposed cards in the tableau (the bottom card of each column) are available for play. As the aces become available, they are placed in a row above the tableau to serve as foundations. The aim is to build up ascending suit sequences from ace to king on the foundations.

Only one card may be moved at a time, either on to a foundation or on to an exposed card in the tableau in descending suit sequence. You are also permitted to move exposed cards from the tableau to the reserve, provided that the reserve never exceeds eight cards. If a column becomes vacant, the space may only be filled with an available king.

Florentine

Deal out five cards face upwards in the form of a cross. Deal a sixth card, also face up, above and to the left of the cross. This is the first of the foundations. The other three cards of the same rank, when they become available, are placed in the other three corners.

The aim is to build up the foundations in ascending suit sequence. If, for example, the first foundation is the 10 of clubs it will be built up in the sequence 10, J, Q, K, A, 2, 3, 4, 5, 6, 7, 8, 9 of clubs, and the other foundations will be similarly built up from 10 to 9 in their respective suits.

Deal cards from the stock one at a time. If eligible, they may be played on to a foundation or may be played on to one of the four outer cards of the cross in descending sequence regardless of suit. Cards may not be played on to the centre card of the cross.

Cards that are not playable either on to a foundation or on to the cross go face up on a rubbish pile.

If one of the outer cards of the cross is removed, either on to a foundation or on to another outer card, the space may be filled with the top card of the rubbish pile or, if you prefer, you may move the centre card of the cross into the space and then fill the centre space from the rubbish pile.

When all the stock has been dealt out, you may turn the rubbish pile for a second deal, but after that no more redeals are allowed.

Flower Garden

Shuffle the pack thoroughly and deal out six 'fans' of six cards each, face upwards.

These are the flower-beds forming the garden. The remaining sixteen cards, which may be held in the hand or spread out on the table, are known as 'the bouquet'.

The aim is to get out the aces as foundations and to build on them in ascending suit sequences from ace to king.

The exposed (rightmost) card of each bed and all the cards in the bouquet are available for play. They may be played on to a foundation or they may be built on to exposed cards in the garden in downward sequence, regardless of suit.

You may transfer a sequence from one bed to another, provided that the descending sequence is maintained. If a flower-bed is completely cleared the space may be filled by any available card or by a sequence from another bed.

Four-Leaf Clover

Remove all the 10s from the pack – they are not required in this game.

Shuffle the remaining forty-eight cards thoroughly and then deal sixteen cards face upwards in four rows of four.

You may discard from this array any king, queen and jack of the same suit if they all appear. You may also discard any two or more of the other cards of any suit if they add up to fifteen. For example, the 9 and 6 of clubs, or the ace, 2, 5 and 7 of hearts.

After discarding, deal more cards to fill the spaces.

The objective is to discard all forty-eight cards.

Gaps

Deal out the whole pack face upwards in four rows of thirteen. Remove the four aces from the array – they play no further part in the game.

This will leave four gaps. Each gap may be filled by transferring there the card that is of the same suit as the card to the left of the gap but is the next higher in rank. So, for example, a gap with the 7 of clubs to its left will be filled by the 8 of clubs.

Each move, of course, will leave another gap somewhere in the layout, which may be filled in the same way.

Whenever a gap occurs at the leftmost end of a row, it may be filled with any 2. You should try to do this as soon as possible, because the objective is to complete a sequence across the rows from 2 to king in each suit.

A gap with a king to its left cannot be filled. Sooner or later you will be blocked because all four gaps will have kings to their left. When this happens, gather up all the cards – except for cards already in the proper sequence starting with a 2 at the leftmost end of a row.

Shuffle the cards you have gathered up and deal them out once more, completing the four rows of thirteen, but leaving a gap after each sequence that you left on the table from the previous deal. This will allow you to add one card to each sequence, by transferring into the gaps, and this will start you going again.

Repeat the sequence of gathering and redealing when play again becomes blocked. You are permitted a total of three deals.

Golf

Deal five rows of seven cards face upwards, overlapping the rows so as to leave the values of all cards visible. This is the tableau or 'the links'.

From the remaining stock, deal out one card at a time face upwards on to a single pile. On to the top card in this pile you may play the exposed card at the bottom of any column in the tableau if it is the next in sequence upwards or downwards regardless of suit. You may continue building until no further exposed cards are available. For example, on a 7 you might be able to play 6, 5, 6, 7, 8, 9, 10, 9 in that order.

For the purposes of building, an ace is counted low and a king high. When a king is played no further cards may be played on it.

When all the stock has been dealt, count the number of cards remaining in the tableau. That is your 'score for the hole'. If you clear the tableau before dealing out all the cards from the stock, you get a negative score of the number of cards remaining in the stock.

The golf enthusiast will play eighteen 'holes', adding up his score for the full round.

King Albert

Forty-five cards are dealt out face upwards to form the tableau. First, a row of nine. Then, overlapping this, a row of eight starting from the second card of the previous row. Then a row of seven, a row of six, and so on. The seven remaining cards, known as 'The Belgian Reserve', may be held in the hand or laid out face upwards underneath the tableau.

All the cards in the reserve as well as the exposed cards in the tableau (the bottom card of each column) are available for play. As the aces become available, they are placed above the tableau as foundations, to be built up in ascending sequence according to suit.

Only one card may be moved at a time, either on to a foundation or on to an exposed card in the tableau in descending alternate-colour sequence. If a column becomes vacant, the space may be filled with any available card. If you wish you may transfer cards back from the foundation to the tableau – provided that they fit in the descending alternate-colour sequence.

Kings and Queens

Deal out the whole pack one card at a time face upwards on to four waste piles. You may choose which pile you place each card on.

As the aces appear, place them in a row above the waste piles and as the 2s appear place them in a row above the row of aces. The aces and 2s form foundations to be built up in ascending order with alternating colours and alternating numbers. So a red ace is followed by a black 3, followed by a red 5, and so on. A black 2 is followed by a red 4, followed by a black 6, and so on.

You may only deal out the pack once, building from the waste piles whenever you can. If you are successful, the end result will be four piles of cards with kings at the top and four piles with queens at the top.

Klondike (Canfield)

In the United Kingdom, *Klondike* is perhaps better known as *Canfield*, and is one of the best known and most popular patience games.

Shuffle the pack well, and deal out twenty-eight cards in the following manner. First, a row of seven with the first card face upwards and the rest of the row face downwards. Then a row of six, with the first card face upwards and overlapping the second card of the previous row. Continue in this way with a row of five, a row of four, and so on, each row overlapping the face-down cards of the previous row and the first card of each row being laid face upwards. The remaining cards are placed face downwards to form the stock.

The face-up card at the bottom of each column is available for play. As aces become available either in the tableau or from the stock they are placed in a row above the tableau to form foundations. The aim is to build up on the foundations complete sequences from ace to king of each suit.

Turn over one card at a time from the stock. If it is not playable on to a foundation or on to the tableau, place it face upwards on a waste pile. The top card of the waste pile is always available to be played on to a foundation or on to the tableau.

On the columns of the tableau you build descending sequences of cards of alternate colours – for example, red jack on black queen, black 10 on red jack, red 9 on black 10, and so on. The bottom card of each column is available to be played on to a foundation and the sequence of face-up cards in any column may be transferred as a whole to another column if this operation will form a longer sequence.

When a complete column is cleared, the space may be filled only with a king or with a sequence which has a king as its top card.

The stock may only be played through once. The game rarely works out.

Labyrinth

Take the four aces from the pack and set them out as foundations. The objective of the game is to build up these foundations in ascending sequence from ace to king according to suit.

Below the foundations deal a row of eight cards face upwards. Build any of these cards that will fit, on to the foundations. Deal from the stock to fill any spaces that result, and do any more building that is then possible. Continue to build and fill until you can do no more.

Then deal another row of eight cards face upwards below the previous row. Build on to the foundations from these cards and from the first row if possible. You may fill spaces in the lower row from stock, but you may no longer fill spaces in the top row.

When you become stuck again, deal a further row of eight cards, and proceed in the same way until all the cards have been dealt.

You may only build with exposed cards – that is the top and bottom card of each column. Playing the top card of a column leaves the card below exposed, and playing the bottom card of a column leaves the card above exposed.

When the play becomes blocked, you are given the privilege of playing one card from any row to a foundation. Even with this privilege, the game is very difficult to get out.

Matching Pairs

This is a very simple game to fill a spare couple of minutes.

Deal out nine cards face upwards in three rows of three. Remove any matching pairs of cards of the same rank and deal more cards to fill the spaces.

Whenever you get nine cards without any matching pairs, you are allowed to deal a tenth card. If this matches one of the nine, it will allow you to remove the pair and set the game going again. But if this tenth card does not match any of the nine, the game is blocked and you have lost.

Monte Carlo

This game is also known as *Weddings* or *Double and Quits*. It is a simple, straightforward game in which the aim is to match up and remove all the cards in pairs.

Shuffle the pack thoroughly and deal out twenty cards, face upwards, in four rows of five cards each. You may remove any two cards of the same rank that are adjacent horizontally, vertically or diagonally – but you may only remove two cards at a time. After removing them, close up the spaces by moving cards from right to left and fill vacant spaces at the rightmost end of a row by transferring cards from the leftmost end of the row beneath. In this way, you keep the cards in the same sequence in which they were dealt originally, and you end up with two spaces at the rightmost end of the bottom row.

Deal two more cards from the stock to fill these spaces, then repeat the process of removing an adjacent pair and moving the other cards to fill up the spaces.

Continue in this way until all the cards have been removed in pairs (and the game is thus won) or until the game is blocked because there are no adjacent pairs that can be removed.

Easier Monte Carlo is the same except that you deal out twenty-five cards in five rows of five. The extra row means that this version of the game works out more often.

Ninety-One

In this game an ace counts as one, a jack as eleven, a queen as twelve and a king as thirteen.

Deal thirteen piles of four cards, all face upwards, and add up the total value of all the top cards. The aim is to make a total of 91, and to do so you may move the top card from any pile to the top of any other pile. Keep doing this until you achieve the required total.

This game will, of course, always work out – so you should make it your aim to see how quickly you can do it. A complete sequence of cards from ace to king is one way of achieving the total of 91 but there are many other ways.

Odd or Even

Discard from the pack all the court cards. Shuffle the remaining forty cards and deal them one at a time face upwards in a row. Whenever two adjacent cards are both odd or both even throw them out.

The objective is to throw out all forty cards in odd or even pairs.

Number Eleven

Deal out face downwards twelve piles of four cards, in three rows with four piles in each row. Turn the top card of each pile face upwards. The remaining four cards are kept as a reserve.

Remove any two cards with pips adding up to eleven (e.g. an ace and a 10, a 3 and an 8, a 4 and a 7). Court cards do not count in making elevens, but when a jack, queen and king all appear, the three of them can be removed together.

When all the elevens and court card trios have been removed, turn up the top cards of the piles you removed them from and continue as before. When a pile is completely cleared, the space may be filled from the reserve.

The aim is to be able to remove all the cards.

Pairs

Deal twelve piles of four cards face downwards, and put the remaining four cards on one side as a reserve.

Turn over the top card of each pile and look for pairs of cards of the same rank – two 5s, for example, or two queens. Remove any such pairs, turn up the cards that were underneath them, and look for more pairs.

As soon as any pile is used up, fill the space with one of the cards from the reserve pile.

The aim is to sort the whole pack into pairs, but you will only manage it if the cards from the reserve are among the last to go.

Perpetual Motion

This easy game is a real test of patience – and stamina! It will almost always work out eventually, but it may take a few hours to do so.

Shuffle the pack thoroughly, and deal four cards face up in a row from left to right.

If two or more cards have the same value, move one on top of the other *from left to right*.

Now deal a second set of four cards on top of the first four. Again if any two or more have the same value, move one on top of the other from left to right. If such a move exposes another card that has the same value as the top card of another pile, this card too may be moved in the same way.

Continue like this, dealing four cards at a time and moving cards that match, until all the cards have been dealt. Then pick up the piles *from right to left*, i.e. put pile 4 on top of pile 3, put this double pile on top of pile 2, and this pile on top of pile 1. Pick up all the cards, turn them over and start dealing in fours once again, from left to right, moving matching cards as before.

After several turns, you may find that you deal out four cards of the same value across the tops of the four piles. This is what you have been waiting for. Remove these four cards and set them aside. Continue with the remaining cards.

The aim is to eliminate all the cards in such groups of four.

Poker Patience

Shuffle the pack well and then deal out twenty-five cards, one at a time, face upwards on the table. After the first card, the others must be placed next to a card already on the table either horizontally, vertically or diagonally. But you must end up with a rectangular array consisting of five rows with five cards in each.

To find out your score, consider each of the five rows and then each of the five columns as a poker hand and award yourself points as follows:

Straight Flush (five consecutive cards in the same suit)	30
Fours (four cards of the same rank)	16
Straight (five consecutive cards, not all the same suit)	12
Full House (three of one rank, two of another)	10
Threes (three cards of the same rank)	6

Flush (five cards of the same suit, not consecutive)	5
Two Pairs	3
One Pair	1

(Aces may count as high – one more than king – or low – one less than 2.)

Obviously there is a great element of skill in deciding where to lay down the cards as you deal them. The highest possible score theoretically is 230 but in actual play any score over 100 is praiseworthy.

Puss in the Corner

Remove the aces from the pack and lay them down face upwards to make four foundations, arranged in a square. The remainder of the pack forms the stock.

The objective of the game is to build up on the foundations ascending sequences of cards of the same colour (though not necessarily of the same suit) from ace to king.

Deal out the stock, one card at a time. Any card that is not playable on to a foundation is played on to any one of four face-up waste piles which are formed in the course of play at the four corners of the foundation square.

If the patience has not worked out when the last card of the stock has been dealt, you are permitted one more deal. Gather together the four waste piles in any order, without shuffling, to form a new stock which is used for the second deal.

Pyramid

Deal twenty-eight cards face upwards in seven rows to form a pyramid, beginning with one card at the top. Each card is then overlapped by two cards in the row below, except for the seven cards in the bottom row which are exposed and available for play. The remainder of the pack forms the stock.

Any two exposed cards in the pyramid that total thirteen may be discarded. For this purpose, aces count as one, jacks as eleven, and queens as twelve. Kings count as thirteen and may be removed as soon as they are exposed without having to be paired. The objective of the game is to discard all the cards in this way.

Deal from the stock one card at a time. Cards that can not be used to make thirteen go face upwards on a single waste pile. A thirteen may be made up of:

(a) a stock card and the top card of the waste pile
(b) a stock card and an exposed card in the pyramid
(c) the top card of the waste pile and an exposed card in the pyramid
(d) two exposed cards in the pyramid.

The stock may only be dealt once. No redeals are permitted.

Quadrille

Shuffle the pack well and deal one card at a time face upwards on to a single waste pile. As aces and 2s turn up, place them to form foundations, as shown below, in the shape of a quadrille.

```
    A H   2 H

2 S           A C

A S           2 C

    2 D   A D
```

Each of these foundations is to be built up according to suit with either odd cards only or even cards only. Thus: A, 3, 5, 7, 9, J, K and 2, 4, 6, 8, 10, Q.

When you come to the end of the stock, turn over the waste pile and redeal. A total of three deals is permitted.

If you are successful each king will end up with his queen at his side.

The Queen and Her Lad

Place the queen of hearts at the top of the pack and the jack of hearts at the bottom. The aim is to bring the queen and the jack together by eliminating all the cards between.

Deal the cards face upwards in a row, beginning of course with the queen.

You may remove any card that comes between two other cards of the same suit or the same rank. You may also remove any pair of cards (of the same suit or of the same rank) which lie between two others of the same suit or rank.

Say, for example, you have the sequence 5 of clubs, 7 of diamonds, 7 of hearts, jack of clubs, 5 of diamonds. You may remove the two 7s because they come between a pair of clubs. This leaves 5 of clubs, jack of clubs, 5 of diamonds. You may now remove the jack of clubs as it comes between a pair of 5s.

Although the principle of the game is simple, the queen very rarely gets her lad!

Red Ace, Black Deuce

Remove from the pack the ace of hearts, king of clubs, ace of diamonds and king of spades. Place them face upwards in a row in that order. These four cards form the foundations to be built upwards from the aces and downwards from the kings in a sequence of alternating colours. Thus a red ace will be followed by a black 2, followed by a red 3 and so on. A black king will be followed by a red queen, followed by a black jack, and so on.

Deal out from the pack one card at a time on to any of four waste piles, building from the waste piles on to the foundations whenever a card will fit.

When you get to the end of the pack, you are allowed to put the waste piles one on top of another to form a new stock which you may then deal out again in the same way.

No further deals are permitted. If you are successful you will end with four completed foundation piles, two topped by red kings and the other two topped by black aces.

Roll Call

Deal the cards one at a time face upwards on to a waste pile. As you deal, count 'Ace, two, three four, . . .' and so on up to the king, then starting again from the ace. If the rank of the card you deal on to the waste pile corresponds with your call, that card is a 'hit' and is removed.

The objective of the game is to hit and thus remove every card from the pack.

When all the cards have been dealt, pick up the waste pile, turn it over and continue dealing. Resume your count from where you left off at the end of the previous deal.

You may have as many deals as necessary.

Russian Patience

Deal out four cards face upwards in a row. This is the tableau. If there are two or more cards of the same suit throw out all but the highest of that suit. Fill the spaces from the stock and throw out any more if you can.

Repeat this until you have cards of four different suits showing. Cover these four cards with four more cards from stock. Again throw out all but the highest card of each suit, including in this process any cards that get uncovered. A space may be filled by the top card of one of the other three piles – thus, of course, uncovering another card.

When you have gone as far as you can, and you again have cards of four different suits showing, deal four more cards from the stock to cover them, and repeat as before.

If the game works out for you, you will be left with just the four aces in the tableau and all the other cards thrown out.

Seven Up

In this game the jacks count as eleven, the queens as twelve, and the kings as thirteen.

Deal out the cards one at a time face upwards in a row. Any 7s that are dealt are removed as are any two or more adjacent cards that add up to seven or a multiple of seven.

The aim is to remove all the cards of the pack.

Sir Tommy and Lady Betty

The old favourite *Sir Tommy* is said to be the original patience game from which all the others are derived.

The aim is to build up four ascending sequences from ace to king, regardless of suit and colour.

Deal out the cards one at a time, on to any of four face-up waste piles. When the aces turn up they are used to form four foundations above the waste piles.

You build on these foundations, placing any 2 on any ace, any 3 on any 2, and so on. You may play the top card of any waste pile on to a foundation in this way, but you are not permitted to transfer cards from one waste pile to another. The cards are dealt out only once – you get no second chance.

This game involves a certain amount of skill as well as luck, but if you are careful to avoid covering low cards with high cards in the waste piles, you should be successful very often.

A variation on this game is called *Lady Betty* and there are two differences:

(a) On each of the foundations you have to build up an ascending sequence from ace to king of cards *of the same suit*.

(b) You are allowed to have six waste piles.

Spades

The aim is to remove all the spades from the pack.

Shuffle the pack well and deal out the cards in packets of four face upwards on to a waste pile. If the top card of the waste pile is a spade throw it out, and if this reveals another spade beneath throw that one out too.

When you have dealt out all the cards, pick up the waste pile, shuffle and redeal, proceeding as before. Less than four cards at the end of the deal are turned over as one packet.

You are allowed a total of seven deals altogether. To be successful you must have thrown out all thirteen spades by the time you get to the end of the seventh deal.

Ten, Twenty, Thirty

Shuffle the pack thoroughly, and deal four cards in a row face upwards on the table.

If any three adjacent cards add up to either ten, twenty or thirty (jacks, queens and kings all counting ten each and aces counting one) you may remove them and deal three more cards in their places.

If you do not have three adjacent cards that add up to ten, twenty or thirty you may, if you wish, move the card on the rightmost end of the row to the leftmost end of the row. (You may repeat this move as often as you like, at any stage of the game.)

If you still do not have three adjacent cards that add up to ten, twenty or thirty, deal a fifth card to the rightmost end of the row. If that does not enable you to remove any of the cards, deal a sixth and so on.

The aim is to remove all the cards.

Tower of Hanoy

This game is played with only nine cards – the 2 to 10 of any suit. Shuffle the nine cards and deal them face upwards in three rows of three. The aim is to move the cards until they are arranged in a single column from 10 down to 2.

You may move only one card at a time from the bottom of any column to the bottom of one of the other columns, but only if the card it goes below is of higher rank. When a column becomes vacant, the space may be filled with the bottom card of either of the other two columns.

Tsarina

Deal out the first five cards from the pack face upwards in the form of a cross. Put the next card face upwards at the top left corner. This card together with the other three cards of the same rank form the foundations which are to be built up in ascending suit sequence.

Deal out from stock one card at a time face upwards on to a waste pile. The card on the top of the waste pile and the exposed cards in the cross are all available for building on foundations. The cards in the cross may also be built on – in descending sequence regardless of suit. Cards may be moved from one part of the cross to another if they will fit the sequence. Any vacant spaces in the cross are filled from the waste pile.

When all the stock has been dealt out, turn over the waste pile. Deal out the first two cards. If either is playable you may continue the deal. But if neither is playable, you have failed.

The following games in this chapter require two packs of cards.

Forty Thieves

Legend has it that this is the game with which Napoleon Bonaparte whiled away his last hours, for which reason it is sometimes called *Napoleon At St. Helena.*

Shuffle two packs of cards thoroughly and deal out forty cards in four overlapping rows of ten cards each. Overlap the cards so that all the values are visible. This is the tableau, and the lowest card in each column is available for play.

Whenever an ace becomes available, it goes as a foundation in a row above the tableau. These eight foundations are to be built up in ascending sequence from ace to king according to suit.

Deal one card at a time from the stock. A card may be built on to a foundation, or on to the tableau in descending suit sequence. Unplayable cards go face upwards on a single waste pile.

Available cards in the tableau may likewise be played on to foundations or on to other columns in the tableau, but only one card at a time may be transferred in this manner.

When a complete column in the tableau is cleared, the space may be filled by any one available card from another column or from the waste pile.

A lot of careful planning is required if the game is to work out.

Sultan

Remove an ace of hearts and all eight kings from the two packs and arrange them in three rows of three cards with the ace of hearts in the centre of the top row and a king of hearts in the centre of the middle row.

The central king of hearts is the sultan, and he remains uncovered throughout the game. The eight cards surrounding him are the foundations to be built up in ascending suit sequence to the queen.

On either side of the foundations deal four face up cards. These eight cards form the reserve.

Deal from the stock one card at a time. Cards that cannot be built on to the foundations go face upwards on a single waste pile. The top card of the waste pile and the eight cards in the reserve are always available for building on to foundations. When a card is used from the reserve, the space may be filled either with the top card of the waste pile or the top card from the stock, but you need not fill the space immediately.

When the stock is exhausted, turn over the waste pile and redeal. You are only allowed to do this twice.

If the game works out you will finish with the sultan surrounded by his harem (the eight queens).

Spider

The objective is to build eight complete descending sequences from king to ace, regardless of suit or colour. What makes this game of patience rather different is that there are no foundations and the building of sequences is done entirely within the tableau.

Shuffle two packs of cards together and deal out four overlapping rows of ten cards, the first three rows being face downwards and the last row face upwards, thus forming ten columns.

The exposed card at the end of each column is available. An exposed card may be built on to any other column in descending sequence, regardless of suit or colour. When a face-down card is exposed, it is turned face upwards. When a complete column becomes vacant, the space may be filled by any exposed card or proper sequence of cards from another column.

When all possible moves have been made and any spaces filled, deal another ten cards from the stock, one at the end of each column.

Continue in this way, making all moves possible and filling in any vacant columns before dealing another ten cards from stock. (The last deal will consist of only four cards, to the ends of the first four columns.)

Whenever you build a complete sequence from king to ace, it is removed from the tableau. To be successful you must remove eight such sequences.

Miss Milligan

Using two packs of cards the aim of this game is to build up on the eight aces as foundations complete suit sequences from ace to king.

Deal out eight cards face upwards in a row. These cards will form the bases of eight columns of overlapping cards as the tableau. If any of these cards is an ace, place it above the row as a foundation. Any other exposed card may be transferred to a foundation if it will fit or built on the end of another column in descending alternate colour sequence – for example, black 9 on red 10, etc. When building on another column a sequence of cards may be moved as a whole. The space left when a column becomes empty may be filled only by a king or by a sequence headed by a king.

When you have made all the moves you can, deal another row of eight cards, overlapping the end of each column (or filling in any spaces). Once again, make any moves that are possible either to foundations or from one column to another.

Continue in this way until all the cards have been dealt. Then you are allowed to remove any one card or any proper sequence of cards from the end of any column to a temporary reserve. This makes the card above available for play. The card or cards in the reserve are also available for play. This process, which is known as 'waiving', may be repeated whenever the reserve becomes empty.

Giant

This game is similar to *Miss Milligan*, apart from three differences:

(a) When a column becomes vacant, the space may be filled by any card or sequence, not just by a king or king sequence.
(b) Cards may be transferred back from the top of foundations to the ends of columns if they will fit and if it will help.
(c) No 'waiving' is allowed.

King's Way

Take out the eight kings from two packs of cards and place them in a row. Shuffle the remaining cards thoroughly and deal four rows of eight cards face downwards underneath the kings. Then deal a fifth row face upwards. The remaining cards form the stock.

The aim is to remove all the cards underneath the kings on to a waste pile to leave the kings' way clear.

Deal from the stock one card at a time to a waste pile, comparing each card with the face-up cards in the tableau. If any of the face-up cards is one less or one more but of opposite colour it can be removed and added to the waste pile. For example, if you deal the 5 of clubs, a red 4 or a red 6 may be removed from the tableau. The face-down card thus exposed may be turned over. Then see if any more can be added to the waste pile, continuing in ascending or descending sequence and alternate colours. When no more cards can be removed from the tableau, continue by dealing another card from the stock to the waste pile.

Aces are given special treatment. An exposed ace in the tableau may only be removed when you deal a 2 of the opposite colour. When you deal an ace from the stock to the waste pile, only a 2 of the opposite colour can be removed from the tableau. If there is no such 2 available, you must put the ace aside on a separate pile.

If the kings' way has not been cleared by the time you reach the end of the stock, turn over the waste pile and then count the number of aces in the separate pile. That is the number of cards you may take from the waste pile to use in a second attempt to clear the kings' way. But after this you are allowed no further replays.

Haden

Shuffle two packs of cards thoroughly and deal out twelve piles of eight cards, all face downwards except for the top card of each pile. The remaining eight cards are dealt out singly face upwards, forming the reserve.

Remove any two cards with pips adding up to eleven (for example, an ace and a 10, a 2 and a 9, a 4 and a 7). Court cards do not count in making elevens but when a jack, queen and king all appear the three of them may be removed.

The cards in the reserve may be used in making elevens and court card trios to be removed, but in practice you will find that the longer you can go without using the reserve cards the more successful you will be.

After removing cards turn up the top cards of the piles you removed them from. Continue in the same way until you are blocked or until you are successful in removing all the cards.

Windmill

From two packs of cards take any ace and place it face upwards as the central foundation. Then deal out two cards in a row to the left of the ace, two to the right, two above it and two below. These cards, all face upwards, represent the sails of the windmill.

The aim of the game is to build up on the central ace four successive 13-card sequences from ace to king, regardless of suit or colour. At the same time, the first four kings that come into play are placed between the sails of the windmill as foundations, and on each of these foundations is built a descending sequence from king to ace, again regardless of suit or colour.

Deal from the stock one card at a time. If it will not fit on any of the foundations it goes face upwards on a waste pile. A card may also be played on to a foundation from the sails or from the top of the waste pile. When a card is taken from the sails, the space may be filled by either the top card of the waste pile or the top card of the stock, but you do not need to fill the space immediately.

The top card of any king foundation may be transferred to the central foundation – or vice versa – if required. This is often an important part of the strategy, as it is important to build as quickly as possible on the central foundation. But only one card at a time may be transferred in this manner, and the kings themselves may never be transferred.

The stock is dealt out only once.

2 BOARD GAMES

CHESS BOARD GAMES

Equipment: For these games you need a chess or draughts/checkers board and up to 32 pieces.

Eight Men

Take eight pawns – or counters or coins or peanuts – and arrange them on the board so that no two are on the same line in any direction, vertically, horizontally or diagonally. Here is one way of doing it. There are several others.

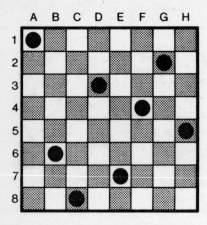

Queen's Question

What is the smallest number of queens that can be placed on a chessboard so as to command or occupy all squares.

(Answer on page 178.)

Roving Rook

A rook can travel any number of squares either sideways or up or down. If you place a rook in one of the four centre squares on the chessboard, what is the minimum number of moves it needs in order to pass over all the squares on the board and return to the start? Try it six times over different routes, and compare your lowest score with the solution on page 178.

Chess Routes

Place a piece, any piece, in the top left-hand square of the board. If the piece is allowed to move only one square at a time – either to the right, or diagonally down and to the right, or down – and if it travels all the way to the bottom right-hand square, how many different routes could it take to get there?
(Answer on page 178.)

Jumpers

Position fourteen pieces around the border of the board on the white squares; put ten more pieces inside them on the next line of white squares.
Start with any man jumping forward or backward diagonally. Remove the man jumped. The jumping man must always land on the square immediately beyond the man jumped. However, any number of squares can intervene between the start of the jump and the man to be jumped. The object is to end up with only one man.
(Solution on page 178.)

Eight Queens

As you know, in chess a queen can move any number of squares in any direction – up, down, sideways, or diagonally. Take eight pawns and imagine they are all queens. Can you arrange them on the chess board so that no queen can take any of the others?
(Solution on page 178.)

The Fifteenth Man

Put fourteen pieces around the border of the board on the white squares. Place a fifteenth man on any unoccupied square and jump as in *Jumpers*. Continue until only one man remains.

(Solution on page 179.)

Five and Three

Equipment: 5 discs and 3 spikes

The 'board' in this game consists of three spikes, but you can play the game without a board if you prefer. The 'pieces' consist of five different-sized discs, but you can't play the game without them. At the beginning of the game the discs should be positioned in decreasing size on the first spike:

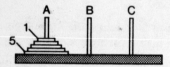

The challenge of the game is this: by always moving a disc on to an empty pile, or on top of a larger disc, can you transfer the whole of the pile of five discs on to another pile? You are only allowed to move one disc at a time.

(Solution on page 179.)

DARTS

Equipment: Dartboard and set of 3 darts.

Solo Darts

In the standard game of solo darts your aim is to reduce a starting score – usually 301, 501 or 1001 – to exactly zero. Darts in the inner bull score 50 and in the outer bull 25. Darts in a sector score according to the sector number, unless they land in the outer 'doubles' ring, when they score double the number, or the inner 'trebles' ring, when they score three times the number. The game must end with a double that brings the score down to exactly 0. (The inner bull counts as a double, of course, because it's double 25.)

301 is the game preferred by most solo darts players and six is the lowest number of shots needed for a perfect game.

Round the World

Your aim is to throw a dart into each of the sectors of the board in order from 1 to 20. Doubles and trebles are allowed, as long as they are in the right sector.

Play using three darts for each turn. In the first turn you must score a double (any one will do), a 1 and a 2. In the second turn you must score a 3, a 4, and a 5, in the third a 6, a 7 and an 8 – and so on. Each group of three numbers counts as one turn. If you fail to complete a turn correctly, you must repeat those three throws until you succeed.

The minimum number of turns needed to move right round the clock is seven. How close can you get to this?

Shanghai

This is a variation of *Round the World*. In your first turn you should aim to throw all three darts into sector 1. Score all singles, doubles and trebles at their actual value – but only if they land in the right sector. Even if none of your darts has hit the right sector, retrieve them all and move on to your next turn. In your second turn throw all three darts into sector 2 and again score them at their actual value if they land in the sector you are aiming at. Continue in this way all the way round to 20, keeping a running total of your score. What is the highest score you can reach?

Fives

In each turn you throw three darts, and you score if – and only if – the sum of your three darts can be divided by five, so if in one turn you hit 3, a double 6 and a 5 (making a total of 20) you score 4 because that's 20 divided by 5, but if in the next turn you hit a 3, a 6 and a 5 (making 14) you score nothing at all because 14 can't be divided by five. The game continues until you have scored 50 points.

Halma

Equipment: Board and 19 pieces

Halma, which was invented in the 1880s, is played on a chequered board with sixteen squares on each side. Each corner has a section bounded with heavy lines, containing thirteen squares. Two opposite corners have an additional heavy line bounding an area with nineteen squares. These areas are the starting and finishing positions and are known as yards.

To play solo halma place 19 pieces in one of the yards and then in 19 moves position them in a symmetrical figure across the board's diagonal.

There are two types of move – steps and hops. A piece may step one square in any direction to a vacant square. Alternatively, a piece may hop over any other piece (whether or not it is of the same colour) if there is a vacant square immediately beyond it. In one move a piece may make several such hops, provided that each hop is over one piece into a vacant square. Steps and hops may not be combined in one move.

The problem can be solved in several hundred ways, and an experienced player should be able to find 50 different solutions without too much difficulty.

Starting position

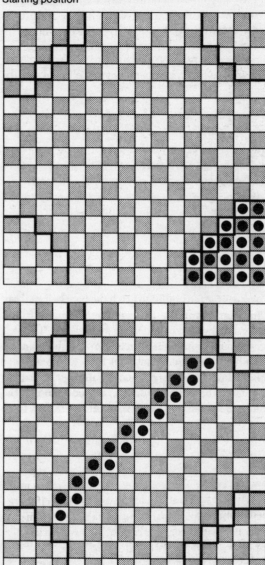

Finishing position

Hare and Hound

Equipment: Board and 2 counters

To play the game you need a counter to be the hare and another to be the hound. You also need a board, which you can draw yourself, looking like this:

Hare starts

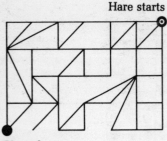

Hound starts
Hare finishes

The object of the game is for the hound to catch the hare before it can get from starting to finishing point, the two counters setting off from opposite corners of the board and moving alternately, hare first. To catch the hare means that the hound is in a position to move to the point on which the hare is standing when it is hound's turn to move. Both counters move one space at a time along connecting lines, but whereas the hare can move anywhere the hound cannot move along diagonals. Neither counter may move between the same two points more than three times in succession.

Knight Errant

Equipment: Board and 24 counters

The board is a simple grid of twenty-five squares (5 × 5) and the 24 counters are knights: a dozen white knights and a dozen black ones. The object of the game is for the white knights to change places with the black knights in the fewest possible number of steps, moving as the knights move in chess.

To begin the game position the knights like this:

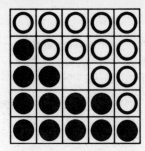

The knights move diagonally – either one square forward and two sideways, or two forward and one sideways – in any direction.

Your goal is to bring the playing men back into the same relative position on the opposite side of the board in the fewest possible moves. While with practice you should finish the game within 50 moves, it is almost impossible to do it in less than 45.

Leapfrog

Equipment: Board and 32 counters

This is a game for which you can draw your own board very simply and use any 32 small objects as counters.

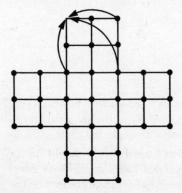

The aim of the game is to remove as many playing pieces as possible from the board by jumping and taking.

To play, place a piece on each point on the board except at the top left hand corner. Pick up a piece and leapfrog into the empty space, removing the piece leapfrogged. As you can see for the first move only one of three pieces can be used to leapfrog into the empty space. Continue leapfrogging, removing pieces as you go. You can leapfrog vertically, horizontally or diagonally, and, with practice, should be able to remove all but one piece from the board.

Light and Shade

Equipment: Board and 48 counters

Using equal numbers of black and white counters on a home-made board of 49 squares (7 × 7), place the blacks to fill three rows and the first three squares of the middle row, the whites to fill the other squares, leaving a single central square vacant. The aim of the game is to move the blacks where whites were and whites where blacks were. Blacks move from left to right or vertically down, by single-square pushes or by jumping as in draughts; whites move from right to left or vertically up in the same manner. There is no need to move counters alternately black and white, and no time limit.

Lucky for Some

Equipment: 12 counters

For this game you need a board that looks like a thirteen-hour clock and twelve counters marked 1 to 12. The board you can imagine and the counters you can make out of bottle tops. To begin the game place the bottle tops in a circle on the table like a clock face but leave a space for an imaginary number thirteen. The aim is to rearrange the bottle tops so that the numbers read anticlockwise instead of clockwise. You may move the tops as you would do for draughts – either into an adjacent empty space or by jumping over one other top into an empty space. You may move backwards or forwards. What is the least number of moves needed to turn the clock backwards?

(You will find the solution on page 179.)

Sam Loyd's Boxes

Equipment: Sets for several of these games have been produced commercially, but you can make your own cardboard versions very simply.

1. Sam Loyd (1841–1911) was America's greatest creator of games and puzzles and the 14–15 Box was probably his most famous – and frustrating – creation:

As you can see, fifteen blocks are arranged in a square box in regular order, but with the 14 and 15 reversed. The game consists of moving the blocks about, one at a time, to bring them back to the present position in every respect except that the error in the 14 and 15 is corrected.

2. Once you have solved the original problem, have a go at this one. Start again with the blocks as in the original puzzle and move them so as to get the numbers in regular order, but with the vacant square at the upper left-hand corner instead of the lower right-hand corner.

3. This time, start with the blocks as before, but turn the box a quarter way round and move the blocks until they are as shown below.

4	8	12	
3	7	11	15
2	6	10	14
1	5	9	13

4. Finally, start as before, then shift the pieces until they form a magic square, the numbers adding to thirty along all vertical and horizontal rows, and the two diagonals.

5. In this box we have nine letters rather than fifteen numbers and the game begins with the box looking like this:

Now the aim of the game is this: moving one block at a time, restore the letters to their correct alphabetical order:

A   B   C

D   E   F

G   H

6. For this game you need a four-armed box that contains twelve movable blocks. The long arms will just hold nine blocks and the short arms two blocks, with room for one at the crossing. Select a

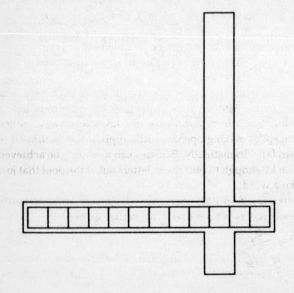

word of twelve letters, and place one letter on each of the blocks, so that the word will read correctly from left to right. Then, in the fewest possible moves, slide the blocks into the other arms of the box, so that the word will read correctly from the top to the bottom of the box. A 'move' is the sliding of one letter any distance within the box, whether you turn a corner or not.

(Solutions on page 179.)

Scrabble

Equipment: Scrabble set

Generally speaking Scrabble is regarded exclusively as a word game for two, three or four players. The play consists of forming interlocking words, in a crossword fashion, on the Scrabble board, using letter tiles with various score values. Each player competes for the highest score by using his letters in combinations and locations that take best advantage of letter values and premium squares on the board.

For solo Scrabble players there are two versions of Scrabble solitaire. In one all the tiles are placed face downwards, well-shuffled, and the player selects seven tiles. He attempts to make a word in the normal way, and scores it. Then he selects from the pool the number of letters necessary, bringing his rack up to its usual complement of seven letters. In this version, he can make openings for himself, just as he would if he was playing in a two-player game.

In the second version, the player attempts to get as high a score as possible at every move. After each move, he puts his remaining letters back into the pool, mixes them thoroughly, and takes seven new letters. Though the concept of making openings still applies, the likelihood of 50-point bonuses falls dramatically. Bonuses can now only be achieved if the player is lucky enough to pull seven letters out of the pool that just happen to make a word.

In both versions of solitaire Scrabble, the player can obviously compare his latest scores with scores from earlier games.

Solitaire

Equipment: English or French solitaire board and 33 or 37 pieces

Solitaire originated in France at least a hundred years ago and came to England towards the end of the eighteenth century. On the English solitaire board there are 33 holes to hold the pieces which are usually either pegs or small marbles.

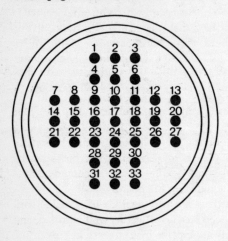

On the French solitaire board there are 37 holes:

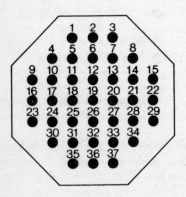

The pieces are moved in the same manner in all solitaire games. Each peg or marble is 'jumped' over an adjoining piece to an empty hole beyond – the piece that has been jumped over is then removed from the board. Pieces may only be moved horizontally or vertically.

A game is considered won only if its objective has been exactly met. For example, the standard game is a success only if the board has been completely cleared of all but one of the pieces.

To play the standard game, begin by removing the piece from the centre hole, then start 'jumping'. You have won when you have removed all but one piece from the board and that piece is now in the centre.

Using the English board here is one way of achieving the right result. There are countless others, and the skill lies in making as few moves as possible:

5 to 17; 12 to 10; 3 to 11; 18 to 6; 1 to 3;
3 to 11; 30 to 18; 27 to 25; 24 to 26; 13 to 27;
27 to 25; 22 to 24; 31 to 23; 16 to 28; 33 to 31;
31 to 23; 4 to 16; 7 to 9; 10 to 8; 21 to 7; 7 to 9;
24 to 10; 10 to 8; 8 to 22; 22 to 24; 24 to 26;
19 to 17; 16 to 18; 11 to 25; 26 to 24; 29 to 17.

The Cross

The game is played using only nine pieces and can be played on either the English or the French board. Place one piece in the centre of the board and put two pieces each side, above and below, to form a cross (i.e. using the English board in holes nos 5, 10, 15, 16, 17, 18, 19, 24 and 29).

The object is to remove eight of the nine pieces from the board, leaving only one at the centre.

The Octagon

Using a French solitaire board and 29 pieces fill all the holes except those at the angles of the board (i.e. not 1, 3, 15, 29, 37, 35, 23, and 9. See diagram on opposite page).

The player tries to end the game so that only one piece – at the centre of the board – remains.

The Corsair

Using a French solitaire board and 29 pieces fill all the holes except at the angles of the board (i.e. not 1, 3, 15, 29, 37, 35, 23 or 9).

The objective is to remove all the pieces except one – which should end up in the hole diametrically opposite the starting hole.

For example, if the game were begun at hole 37 the last piece should be in hole 1.

Shapely Solitaire

Using an English or French solitaire board and 33 or 37 pieces you can create for yourself a whole range of solitaire games simply by choosing a specific pattern for the pieces and then doing your best to achieve it in as few moves as possible.

To give an idea of the possibilities, here are three famous pattern-forming games designed to be played on the French board. Each begins with all 37 pieces in position. The central piece is then removed and you have to play until you are left with pieces in the following formations (see diagram on p. 42 for figure references):

(a) The World – 1, 2, 3, 4, 8, 9, 15, 16, 17, 18, 19, 20, 21, 22, 23, 29, 30, 34, 35, 36 and 37
(b) The Apostles – 1, 3, 4, 8, 9, 15, 19, 23, 29, 30, 34, 35 and 37
(c) The letter 'E' – 1, 2, 3, 5, 11, 18, 19, 20, 25, 31, 35, 36 and 37

You will find suggested solutions on page 180.

3 DOMINO GAMES

The oldest known set of dominoes was discovered in 1922 in the tomb of King Tutankhamen of Egypt (c. 1371–c.1352 B.C.) and can be seen today in the Tutankhamen Museum in Cairo. It seems generally agreed that dominoes actually originated in China and were introduced into Europe by Venetian traders in the fourteenth or fifteenth century A.D. From Italy they were introduced into France, and it is believed that the English first learned about dominoes from French prisoners-of-war during the Napoleonic Wars.

Dominoes are rectangular tiles, made usually from bone, ivory, wood or plastic. A standard European set consists of 28 tiles. The face of each tile is divided by a central line into two equal squares, each of which is either blank or marked with pips from one to six in number. This set is also known as the Double-6 set, as the double-6 is the top domino in the set. All the games and challenges here are played with this set.

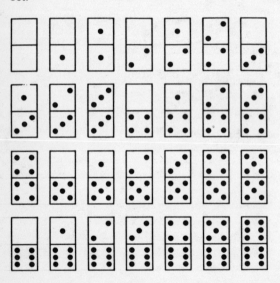

Domino Patience

Shuffle the dominoes face downwards and draw five. Turn these five face upwards and play one of them. Now match either end of your first domino with another from your hand. Continue to play to either end.

Whenever you find that you are left only with dominoes in your hand that will not fit on either end, you must draw an extra domino from those still face down, and continue doing this until you pick one that you can play.

Whenever you manage to play all the dominoes from your hand you have won.

Five's the Limit

This is the same as the previous game except that there is the additional rule that you are never allowed to have more than five dominoes in your hand at any one time.

If you have five unplayable dominoes in your hand you have lost.

Knock-Out

Turn all the dominoes face downwards, shuffle them well, and arrange them end to end in one long line. Keeping them in the same position, turn them all face upwards.

If there are any dominoes whose ends match where they touch, you may 'knock' them out of the line and close up the gap.

Carry on doing this as long as you can. The objective is to knock out every domino. You won't succeed very often, so when you do your sense of satisfaction should be considerable.

Bingo

This game is purely a matter of chance but nevertheless it is quite entertaining.

Start by turning all the dominoes face downwards, shuffle them well and arrange them all in one long row, side by side. Now turn them all face upwards, without disturbing the order.

Starting from the leftmost end of the row, begin counting from 0 to 12, touching a domino as you speak each number. Add the pips on each domino as you do so, and if they match the number you speak, you may remove it from the line.

When you reach 12 start counting from 0 again, and when you get to the end of the row close up all the gaps and continue counting from the leftmost end of the row.

The aim is to remove all the dominoes.

Twelve to Go

Shuffle the dominoes face downwards and draw six of them. Place them face upwards in front of you. The remaining twenty-two dominoes form the stock: put them to one side for the moment.

If, in the six dominoes you have chosen, there are any two dominoes which between them have a total of twelve pips, you may discard them. For example, the 6–2 and 3–1 or the double-six and the double-blank. Put any discarded dominoes into a waste pile and replace them from the stock so that you always have six dominoes in front of you.

If you are able to discard all the twenty-eight dominoes in the set, you have won the game.

Five Columns

Shuffle the dominoes face downwards. Draw off three of them and place them face upwards. These three are your reserve.

Leaving the other twenty-five dominoes face downwards, arrange them in five columns with five dominoes in each column. Turn them all face upwards, keeping them in the same positions.

The domino at the bottom of each column and the three in reserve are all available for play. If the pips on any two available dominoes add up to twelve, you may remove that pair of dominoes and move them to a discard pile.

Discarding a domino from the bottom of a column makes the domino above it available for play. When the last domino from a column is discarded, the bottom domino from any other column may be moved into its place.

The aim of the game is to discard all twenty-eight dominoes.

Seven Towers

Shuffle the dominoes face downwards, draw seven and place them face downwards in a row. Place another seven dominoes face downwards on top of them, then another seven. Place the last seven dominoes face upwards on top of the piles. This gives you seven towers, each composed of four dominoes.

You may discard any pair of the top dominoes whose pips total 12, and turn up the two dominoes that become exposed as a result. When all the dominoes in one of the towers have been discarded, you may not move any other domino into the vacant space.

Success consists in discarding all twenty-eight dominoes, but sadly this is not achieved that often!

One Down

Shuffle the dominoes face downwards and draw four. Turn these four face upwards and lay them down side by side.

Add up the number of pips on each domino. If any domino has exactly one pip less on it than any other domino, it may be discarded. For example, if your dominoes are the 2–1, 4–2, 6–1 and 6–5, then the 4–2 may be discarded as its pip count is one less than the 6–1.

When you have made your discards, draw another four dominoes and place them face upwards on top of the first four (or covering any vacant spaces). Again, if any domino has a pip count one less than another, you may discard it.

Discards may reveal other dominoes that had been covered, and these come into play, possibly making further discards possible. Where you have a choice of discards, it is an advantage to be able to remember which dominoes have been covered.

Continue in this way, drawing another four dominoes whenever you have discarded all the dominoes that you can.

If you are successful you will end with just the double-6, having discarded all the other twenty-seven dominoes.

Double Trouble

Shuffle the dominoes face downwards. Form seven piles of three with all the dominoes face down. Then place a fourth domino face upwards on top of each pile.

The objective of the game is to end up with seven piles with one double at the bottom of each pile and with all four dominoes in the pile being of the same suit. That is, the pile with the double blank at the bottom must have three other blanks in it, the pile with the double-1 at the bottom must have three other 1s in it, and so on.

A domino may be shifted from one pile to another, provided that one of its numbers matches one of the numbers on the domino which it is about to cover. At no time may you have more than five dominoes in any one pile.

Whenever you move a domino and reveal a face-down domino beneath, you can turn the face-down domino face upwards.

You may never have more than seven piles. But if you move all four dominoes from a pile, the space may be filled – but only with a double.

When you have finished, the seven doubles at the bottom of the piles may be in any order in the line.

This game requires a good memory and a lot of concentration.

DOMINO CHALLENGES

First Square

Take 6 dominoes – the 0/0, the 0/1, the 0/2, the 1/1, the 1/2 and the 2/2 – and arrange them in a square, so that each of the four sides of the square contains the same number of pips.

(You will find the solution to this and all the other challenges at the back of the book.)

First Rectangle

For this you'll need the same 6 dominoes – the 0/0, the 0/1, the 0/2, the 1/1, the 1/2, the 2/2, and the same quick-wittedness you've used before. You have got to use the dominoes to create a rectangle but the puzzling part of the challenge comes in making sure that each of the four sides of the rectangle contains precisely the same number of pips.

Giant Square

Make a square using the 10 lowest dominoes in the set – that is the 0/0, the 0/1, the 0/2, the 0/3, the 1/1, the 1/2, the 1/3, the 2/2, the 2/3 and the 3/3 – but you must make sure that the number of pips on each of the four sides of the Giant Square is the same and that none of the joins match.

The Three Rectangles

Take the 15 lowest dominoes in the set (the 0/0, the 0/1, the 0/2, the 0/3, the 0/4, the 1/1, the 1/2, the 1/3, the 1/4, the 2/2, the 2/3, the 2/4, the 3/3, the 3/4, the 4/4) and form 3 separate rectangles of 5 dominoes each so that all the joins are matching.

The Five Lines

With the same 15 dominoes you used to make the Three Rectangles, form 5 lines, with 3 dominoes in each line.

In each of the 5 lines the joins must match and there must be exactly the same number of pips in each line.

The Seven Lines

Take a complete set of dominoes and discard all the pieces in the 6-suit. You are now left with 21 dominoes. Arrange the 21 dominoes in seven lines with 3 dominoes in each line, so that each line contains exactly the same number of pips and all the joins match.

Three More Rectangles

Using the same 21 dominoes, form three rectangles of 7 dominoes each.

The problem is to make sure that all twelve sides – that's to say each of the four sides on each of the three rectangles – contain exactly the same number of pips. It's the trickiest challenge you've had so far, but keep trying and you should succeed.

The Seven Squares

Take all 28 dominoes and make them into seven squares, with each square formed like this:

All the joins in each of the seven squares must match, but to make life even more difficult for you, you can't use the example given here, as one of the actual squares.

The Two Lines

Take the 10 lowest dominoes in the set – the 0/0, the 0/1, the 0/2, the 0/3, the 1/1, the 1/2, the 1/3, the 2/2, the 2/3 and the 3/3 – and arrange them in two lines of 5 dominoes each.

All the joins must match and you must end with a total of 15 pips in each line.

Another Three Rectangles

With the lowest 15 dominoes in the set – the 0/0, the 0/1, the 0/2, the 0/3, the 0/4, the 1/1, the 1/2, the 1/3, the 1/4, the 2/2, the 2/3, the 2/4, the 3/3, the 3/4 and the 4/4 – form three rectangles of 5 dominoes each. Each of the twelve sides (that means all four sides of each of the three rectangles) must contain exactly the same number of pips, but there is no need for the joins to match.

The Three Lines

Discard the 7 dominoes of the 6-suit and use the remaining 21 dominoes to make three lines of 7 dominoes. Each line must contain exactly the same number of pips and the joins must all match.

The Giant Eight

Take the 10 lowest dominoes in the set – 0/0, the 0/1, the 0/2, the 0/3, the 1/1, the 1/2, the 1/3, the 2/2, the 2/3, and the 3/3 – and arrange them to form a rather square figure of eight, like this:

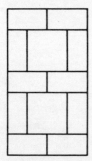

Both the vertical columns (that is the two sides of the figure) and the three horizontal rows (that is the 2 dominoes at the top of the figure, the 2 in the middle and the 2 at the bottom), must contain exactly the same number of pips.

Another Seven Squares

After some easy, not-so-easy and less-than-easy challenges, this one is almost impossible – almost, of course, but not quite. You need all 28 dominoes and you must use them to form seven squares, with 4 dominoes making up each square.

You won't be able to make the number of pips on all 28 sides of the seven squares come to the same total, but what you must do is make sure that the number of pips on each side of any one square is exactly the same.

Double-Crossed

The challenge here is to use all 28 dominoes to make two crosses as in the example below.

The horizontal bars and the vertical bars, each of which contains eight pieces, are each to contain the same number of pips. The direction of the pieces must be exactly as shown here.

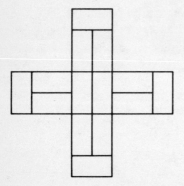

Double-Crossed Again

The game's the same, but the patterns are different.

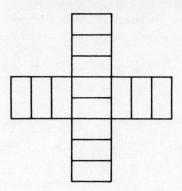

The Arches

Using all 28 pieces, make seven arches of the form shown here. All of the joins are to match in number, and the number of pips on the two horizontal pieces must be equal to the number of pips on the two vertical pieces.

The Heptagon

The challenge here is to form a seven-sided figure so that the four dominoes on each side contain the same number of pips. All the joins must match in number, including those at the angles.

The Magic Square

The 6-by-6 square is the largest solid square that can be made with the Double-6 set. With the eighteen pieces of your choice, form a magic square in which each of the six rows, six columns and the two principal diagonals must contain the same number of pips. Any of the pieces may be laid either horizontally or vertically.

4 FIVESTONES AND FRIENDS

FIVESTONES

Variations of Fivestones games have been played since ancient times and still today are part of traditional cultures all over the world.

In the good old days this pastime involved the use of the knuckle-bones of a sheep – a dead one, of course – or of some other domesticated animal. Today you are more likely to play with a set of coloured wooden or plastic cubes sold as Fivestones or Jacks. Failing that, five dice or five small rounded pebbles will do instead.

The games are normally played in sequence, as described here. If you fail in any game, it is usual to impose the rule that you go back to the beginning and start the sequence again. As, with practice, you become more proficient, you will find that you will be able to progress further and further through the sequence of games without error.

You can play Fivestones at a table but it is much better to play it on the floor from either a squatting or sitting position.

Jockey

Hold the five stones in one hand. Throw them up in the air a little way and try to catch them all on the back of your hand. Throw them up once more and catch them in your palm.

If you catch all five stones, go on to *Twos*. If you catch only some of the stones, go on to *Ones*. If you catch none, start again.

Ones

Scatter all the five stones from your hand on to the floor. Pick up one of them and throw it in the air. Pick up one of the stones from the floor in your throwing hand before catching the thrown stone in the same hand. Transfer the stone you picked up to your other hand. Continue until all the stones have been picked up.

Twos

This game is played in the same way as *Ones*, except that you pick up *two* of the stones from the floor in your throwing hand and catch the thrown stone in the same hand. Transfer the two stones you picked up to your other hand. Then pick up the remaining two stones in the same way.

Threes

This is played in the same way as Twos, except that you pick up three stones on the first throw and the remaining stone on the second throw.

Fours

Fours is played in the same way as Twos and Threes except that you pick up all four stones from the floor in one throw.

Pecks

Throw all five stones in the air and catch them on the back of your hand. Throw them again and catch them in your palm.

If you catch all five, go straight on to the next game. If you catch none, start again. Otherwise, keep all the stones you caught in your hand. Work one of them out so that you can hold it between forefinger and thumb, closing your hand over the other stones in your palm.

Throw this one stone into the air, pick up one stone from the floor with your throwing hand and catch the thrown stone with the same hand. Repeat this until all five stones have been gathered into your throwing hand.

Bushels

Throw all five stones in the air and catch them on the back of your hand. Throw them again and catch them in your palm.

If you catch all five, go straight on to the next game. If you catch none, start again. Otherwise throw all the stones in your hand up in the air and pick one off the floor before catching them all again in the same hand.

Repeat this until you have gathered all five into the same hand.

Claws

Throw all five stones in the air and catch them on the back of your hand.

If you don't succeed in catching any on the back of your hand, start again from the beginning.

If you catch all five on the back of your hand, throw them in the air again and try to catch all five in your palm. If you catch them all, go on to the next game. If you catch none, start again at the beginning.

If you catch some but not all on the back of your hand, leave them there while you pick up all the fallen stones between the fingers of your throwing hand – no more than one stone between any two fingers. Throw the stones from the back of your hand and catch them in your palm. Then manoeuvre the stones between your fingers into your palm too, without using your other hand or dropping any stones.

Ones Under the Arch

Scatter the five stones on the floor, then make an arch near them with your non-throwing hand by touching the thumb and forefinger to the floor. Pick up one stone and throw it into the air. Before catching it again in the same hand, you must knock one of the stones on the floor through the arch. Repeat this until you have knocked all four stones under the arch. Remove the arch, throw again, pick up the four stones in your throwing hand and catch the thrown stone again in the same hand.

Twos Under the Arch

This is similar to Ones Under The Arch, except that you knock two stones under the arch on each throw.

Threes Under the Arch

This is similar to the previous two games except that first you knock three stones under the arch, then one.

Fours Under the Arch

This is the same as before except that you knock all four stones under the arch on one throw.

Stables

Scatter the five stones on the floor. Spread out the fingers and thumb of your non-throwing hand and place it near the stones so that your finger-tips are touching the floor and the palm is raised. The spaces between your fingers represent four stables.

Throw one of the stones in the air. Before catching it again in the same hand you must knock one of the other stones into one of the stables. Repeat this procedure to knock a stone into each stable in turn.

Move away your non-throwing hand. Throw the stone in the air once more, pick up the four stones in the throwing hand and catch the thrown stone in the same hand.

Toad in the Hole

Scatter the five stones on the floor. Place your non-throwing hand near the stones so that the thumb lies straight on the floor with the fingers curled round to form a hole.

Throw one stone in the air and, before catching it again, pick up one of the other stones and drop it into the hole. Repeat this procedure until all four stones have been dropped into the hole.

Move away your non-throwing hand. Throw the stone in the air once more, pick up the four stones in your throwing hand and catch the thrown stone in the same hand.

Backward Ones

Scatter the stones on the floor. Throw one in the air and catch it on the back of your hand. Throw it again from the back of your hand, pick up one of the other stones and catch the thrown stone in the same hand.

Throw up both stones and catch them on the back of your hand. Throw them again from the back of your hand, and pick up another stone before catching the two thrown.

Repeat this procedure with three and then four stones.

Backward Twos

This is the same as *Backward Ones* except that you pick up two stones on each throw.

Backward Threes

This is the same as before except that you pick up three stones and then one.

Backward Fours

This is the same as before except that you pick up all four stones on one throw.

Snake in the Grass

Place four of the stones in a straight line, about six inches (15 cm) apart. Throw the fifth stone in the air and before catching it again in the same hand, move one of the end stones along a route as shown in the illustration.

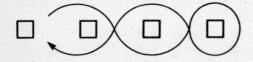

The moved stone must move round the other stones and back to its starting point. You may take as many throws as you like to complete the journey, provided that the stone is moved part of the way on each throw and you don't touch any of the other three stones.

Square Sweep

Place four stones at the corners of an imaginary square, about twelve inches (30 cm) apart. Throw up the fifth stone, pick up all four from the floor, and catch the thrown stone in the same hand.

TIDDLYWINKS

Solo Tiddlywinks

Equipment: Cup, winks and squidger

A game of Tiddlywinks isn't really possible unless there are two of you, so when you're alone and want to play Tiddlywinks you have to split your personality and pretend that two of you are going to play the game. The two players are called Ego and Alter-ego, and if you fancy a three-handed contest Super-ego can join in as well.

Tiddlywinks can be played on the floor but is best played on a table covered with a thick cloth or a piece of felt. The cup, which should be about 1½ inches (4 cm) wide and 1–2 inches (3–5 cm) high, is placed in the centre of the table. Each player chooses a colour and takes six winks, which are small flat discs of plastic, and a squidger, which is a larger disc. A wink is squidged by pressing the edge of one's squidger against the edge of the wink, thus making the wink jump into the air. The object of the game is to be the first player to squidge all one's winks into the cup.

Each player lines his winks up in front of him at an equal distance from the cup. (You've got to watch how Super-ego does this. He is inclined to cheat.) To determine the order of play each player squidges one wink, and the player who gets his wink nearest to the cup is the first to play.

A player may squidge only his own winks and has one squidge per turn except that when he succeeds in potting a wink he is entitled to an extra squidge. Winks are always squidged from where they lie, except when a wink is accidentally squidged off the table when it can be replaced on the nearest point on the edge of the table.

When a wink is covered by another wink, it is said to be squopped. If a player has a wink that is squopped by an opponent's wink he may not squidge it – he must wait until the opponent removes his wink or must attempt to dislodge it by squidging another of his own winks at it.

Successful play requires not only accurate squidging but also the ability to judge when to pot and when to squop. And winning the game is wonderful for the ego.

Wars of the Roses

For this game you need a dozen white winks and a dozen red ones. (If your winks happen to be of different hues you can still play, but you had better give the game a different name.) The game itself represents a battle to the death between the Lancastrians and the Yorkists and is not concluded until one side has totally annihilated the other.

To begin the game, line up the twelve red winks at one end of the table and the twelve white winks at the other end. Either side may start and play alternates between the two warring parties.

If a wink lands on an enemy wink and in any way overlaps it, the enemy wink has been killed and must be removed from the field of action. Whenever an enemy wink is killed the side that achieved the kill gets an extra turn.

If a wink lands next to an enemy wink and touches it, the enemy wink has been wounded. He does not leave the field of action, but can no longer be used in an attack. He can be squidged away from danger, but he cannot be squidged towards his enemy. If a wounded wink inadvertently lands on or touches an enemy wink, the attack does not count.

If a wink is squidged off the table he is deemed 'missing, presumed dead' and cannot return to the field of action.

When all twelve of one side's winks have been killed, the other side is victorious, however few winks happen to be left in its ranks.

Over the Water

Make a paper ring by drawing two concentric circles, one with a radius of 5 ins (12 cm) the other with a radius of 2 in (5 cm). Cut along both lines so that you are left with a paper ring – this is the moat. Position at one end of your table with the cup in the middle of it.

Now line up four red tiddlywinks and four green – or any other colour that takes your fancy – at the other end of the table and you are ready to start. Your aim is to get all the winks into the cup, but will red get there first, or will green?

Start by squidging a red, then a green, and so on, using alternate colours. Any winks that land in the moat are drowned and must be removed from the game. If one wink is even partly covered by another it must stay where it is until the top one is moved. And if any wink lands propped up against the side of the cup it must stay there until knocked down flat on to the table by another wink.

Golf

Your first task in tiddlywinks golf is to make the course on a table top. Find nine eggcups, coffee cups, or napkin rings to act as holes and place them at random on the cloth. Now find some obstacles – pieces of corrugated cardboard, a sponge, balls of crumpled paper, a ball of wool, a book opened and placed face down, and so on. Slip these underneath the tablecloth, positioned at intervals round the course. You can even make life more difficult for yourself by adding a couple of water obstacles in the form of saucers of water and a 'real' bunker made from a handful of sand.

You now have to compete against the clock to see how long it takes you to get one wink round the course and into each of the holes in turn. You may start and finish wherever you like, but you must get the wink into every hole.

MARBLES

Marbles – also known as taws or alleys or bools – are small, hard balls which are usually made from glass but may also be made of clay, stone, wood or other materials.

There are several schools of thought as to the optimal technique of marble propulsion. Some players merely roll them, but dedicated players usually prefer to flick (or 'knuckle') them. To do this, the back of the hand is placed on the ground with the side of the forefinger at right-angles to the required line of flight. A marble is poised in the crease of the top joint of the forefinger and is flicked smartly with the thumb.

If space allows, you can test your strength as a marble knuckler by seeing how far you can propel your marble. If you are looking for a test of marble skill rather than strength, the next three games should suit you.

Marble Bowls

Select nine marbles for this game, four of colour A, four of colour B, and one of colour C. Let us suppose they are red, blue and white respectively. White will be the jack, and red will play against blue, each colour, or team, aiming to place its marbles nearest to the jack.

Roll the jack so that it stops about a yard away. Now bowl red and blue marbles alternately, aiming to get each one as close to the jack as possible. The usual tactics of bowls may be used, such as blocking the other team's path to the jack, knocking opposing marbles out of the way, breaking up a group around the jack, and so on.

If you concentrate on the individual marbles as you play them you will become engrossed in the game and be genuinely surprised when you count up at the end to see whether red or blue has won. Score marks as follows: 5 for a marble touching the jack, then 4, 3, 2 and 1 for the marbles nearest the jack in descending order of distance.

Spangy

Use chalk to mark out an area about 1 ft (30 cm) square. Put one target marble in the middle and one in each corner. Your aim is to claim these marbles by knocking them out of the square. Kneel down about 2 yards (2 metres) away and shoot a marble at the square. If you hit a target you may claim both your shooter and the target, but if you fail to hit a target and your shooter lands in or near the square, you must try to make a span. Keeping your thumb on the shooter, see if you can touch a target with your finger. If you can, you may remove both marbles from the game. If you cannot your shooter must stay where it is and become one of the targets. How many shots will you need to clear the square?

Bounce Eye

Mark a circle of 12 inches (30 cm) in diameter on a newspaper and place it on the floor with a group of 5 marbles in the middle. Now stand over the ring and drop another marble on to the group to see if you can make any marbles roll out of the circle. If your own marble stays in the circle, you must leave it there. And if none of the target marbles rolls out, you must add an extra one to the circle as a penalty. How many drops will you need to clear the circle?

Underneath the Arches

For this game you need six marbles, a tray, a book and a cardboard box (an empty tissue box would be ideal). Cut away one of the long thin sides of the box and then cut five small arches in one of the long cut edges. Mark a number over each arch – 5, 3, 1, 3, 5 in that order. Stand the box at one end of the tray and raise the other end of the tray on the book. All you have to do is roll the marbles down the tray one by one, adding up the score as they disappear underneath the arches. How long will it take you to reach the top score of 30 with your six marbles?

DICE

Beat the Clock

Using two dice, try to throw the numbers 1 to 12 in the correct order. For numbers up to and including 6, you can choose to take the score on either die or on both together – i.e. a throw of 1 or 3 may score 1, 3 or 4, depending on which you need. For number 7 and above, you will have no choice and will have to take the total of both dice.

First Eleven

With two dice it is possible to throw eleven different numbers – 2 to 12 inclusive. How long will it take you to throw these numbers in the correct order?

There are, of course, different ways in which you can throw many of the numbers. These are the variations:

2	1 + 1
3	1 + 2
4	1 + 3, 2 + 2
5	1 + 4, 2 + 3
6	1 + 5, 2 + 4, 3 + 3
7	1 + 6, 2 + 5, 3 + 4
8	2 + 6, 3 + 5, 4 + 4
9	3 + 6, 4 + 5
10	4 + 6, 5 + 5
11	5 + 6
12	6 + 6

Boston Bound

Boston Bound is the solo version of *Going to Boston*, one of the best-known dice games for two or more players using 3 dice. With *Boston Bound* there are only two players: your right hand and your left hand. Not surprisingly, the right hand rolls the dice with his right hand and the left hand with the left. The right hand plays first and begins the game by rolling all three dice at once. He then leaves the die which shows the highest number (if two are equally high, he leaves only one of them) and rolls the other two again. This completes his turn, and his score is the total shown by the three dice. When both hands have done the same in their turn, the player with the higher score is the winner of that round.

A set number of rounds is usually played, and the player who has won most rounds is the winner of the game.

Solo Crag

To play Crag on your own you need 3 dice and you have to invent at least three players and give them names, say Shedrak, Mishak and Abednego, or Athos, Porthos and Aramis, or Bill, Ben and Little Weed. Having decided on your players, you must draw up your score sheet looking like this:

	Harpo	*Groucho*	*Chico*
Ones			
Twos			
Threes			
Fours			
Fives			
Sixes			
Odd Straight			
Even Straight			
Low Straight			
High Straight			
Three of a kind			
Thirteen			
Crag			
Totals			

Before the game begins, there is a preliminary round to determine who will be the first player. Each player throws the dice once, and the player with the highest score will start the game.

The game itself starts with the first player throwing the three dice. He may then, if he wishes, throw one, two or all three dice again. His objective is to obtain one of the following scoring patterns:

1. Ones (scoring one point for each 1 thrown – maximum 3 points)
2. Twos (scoring two points for each 2 thrown – maximum 6 points)
3. Threes (scoring three points for each 3 thrown – maximum 9 points)
4. Fours (scoring four points for each 4 thrown – maximum 12 points)
5. Fives (scoring five points for each 5 thrown – maximum 15 points)
6. Sixes (scoring six points for each 6 thrown – maximum 18 points)
7. Odd Straight (the 1, 3 and 5 – scoring 20 points)
8. Even Straight (the 2, 4 and 6 – scoring 20 points)
9. Low Straight (the 1, 2 and 3 – scoring 20 points)
10. High Straight (the 4, 5 and 6 – scoring 20 points)
11. Three of a kind (all three dice showing the same value – scoring 25 points)
12. Thirteen (a total of thirteen without a double – 2, 5 and 6, or 3, 4 and 6 – scoring 26 points)
13. Crag (a total of thirteen including a double – 1, 6, 6 or 3, 5, 5, or 5, 4, 4 – scoring 50 points)

His score is, of course, recorded on the chart. Each player in his turn throws the three dice and may decide to score with the dice as thrown or to throw one or more again in an attempt to obtain a better score. His score is then recorded and the play passes round the table.

A player may or may not have a choice as to which pattern he scores. Let us say, for example, he has thrown two 4s and a 6: he may choose to score 8 points for Fours or 6 points for Sixes if he has not already scored for either of these patterns. If he has already scored for one of them then he is obliged, this time, to score for the other. If he has already scored for both of these patterns then he must choose some other pattern for which to score nought.

When the dice have passed thirteen times around the table the players will have filled in all thirteen spaces on the score sheet. The player with the highest total score is the winner. The charm of playing this game on your own is that you don't mind losing because you are always on such intimate terms with the winner.

Dice Sentence

The aim of the game is to write an English sentence using letters, spaces and punctuation dictated by the roll of the dice.

Take two dice, a pencil and a sheet of paper. Throw the first die and look along the row with that number in the chart below. Throw the second die to choose a column, and then find out which letter or space or punctuation mark your dice has given you.

		second die					
		1	2	3	4	5	6
	1	A	B	C	D	E	F
	2	G	H	I	J	K	L
first die	3	M	N	O	P	Q	R
	4	S	T	U	V	W	X
	5	Y	Z	.	,	!	?
	6	*	*	*	*	*	*

* Indicates a space. You need the spaces to separate the words in your sentence.

Carry on rolling the dice until you have collected sufficient letters, spaces and punctuation marks to be able to construct a sentence. The sentence doesn't need to be long and it doesn't have to make much sense, but it must be a real sentence and must use all the letters, spaces and punctuation marks the dice have given you. This game won't be like writing *War and Peace*, but it could take you almost as long.

Devil's Dice

To play this diabolical game you need a special set of four dice which you can make quite easily by copying the following patterns onto thin card, cutting them out (along the thick lines) and folding them (along the thin lines) into cubes.

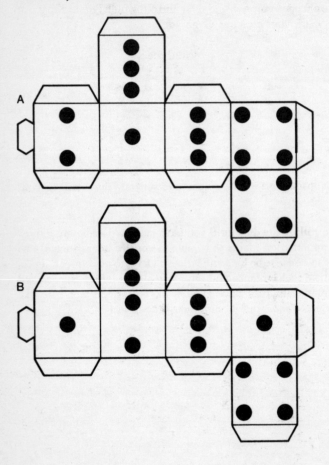

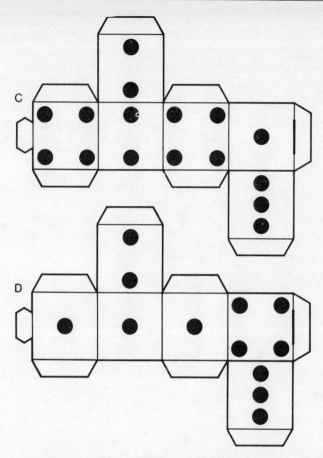

To play the game all you have to do is arrange the dice in a straight line, so that when all four dice are viewed from the top and from underneath and from the front and from the back there is one die with one dot, one with two dots, one with three dots and one with four dots, though not necessarily in that order, visible on each of the four sides being viewed.

It sounds easy, but it isn't. In a year or so, when you still haven't cracked it, you can look at the solution on page 186.

5 COINS AND MATCHES

Whether the challenges in this chapter should be described as games or puzzles is open to debate. What is beyond question is that they are all stimulating solo entertainments and all but a handful of them have specific solutions which can be found at the back of the book, the answers to the coin challenges starting on page 186, the answers to the match challenges on page 194.

COINS

Star Turn

You will need nine coins, a pencil and paper. Begin by drawing a large five-pointed star on a piece of paper.

What you have to do is to put your finger on one crossing or point, pass over the next crossing and place a coin on the crossing or point beyond that. You have to keep doing this until all but one of the crossings and points of the star have been covered with coins.

Four Finger Exercise

Take four coins and place one on the tip of each finger on your right hand. The aim is to manoeuvre them all into a pile on the tip of your first finger. You are not allowed to use your thumb or your other hand – or any other part of your anatomy.

It is not easy but it can be done – after a lot of practice!

Elbow Exercise

Bend your arm backwards so that your knuckles are touching your shoulder. Place a coin on your elbow. Then unbend your arm quickly, bringing your hand down sharply and catch the coin before it reaches the ground.

Done that? Good! Now try with two coins piled on your elbow. Then three. Then four. And so on. The world record is eighteen coins. Can you beat that?

Coins in a Circle

Take six coins and lay them out on the table in two columns like this:

Now all you have to do is make a circle of coins in just three moves. You can only move one coin at a time and once you've moved it to its new position it must be touching at least two other coins.

Coins in a Pyramid

Take ten coins and lay them out on the table in the shape of a pyramid, like this:

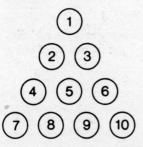

Now move just three of the coins and turn the pyramid upside down.

The H Problem

Take seven coins and arrange them in a pattern to look like the letter H.

As you can see, counting the diagonal lines as well as the vertical and horizontal, you have five rows with three coins in each row. Now add an extra two coins to the pattern and create a new pattern that incorporates ten rows with three coins in each row.

Sixteen Coins

Take sixteen coins and arrange them on the table in four rows of four, all touching, with heads and tail alternating.

Now all you've got to do is rearrange the coins so that the coins in each of the four vertical columns are alike. That is you have to end up with one column of heads, one column of tails, one of heads, one of tails. The only problem is: your hand is only allowed to touch *two* of the sixteen coins!

Star Trek

Draw an eight-pointed star on a large sheet of paper and place a coin, heads up, on point 1, a coin, heads up, on point 3, a coin, tails up on point 6, and a coin, tails up, on point 8, like this:

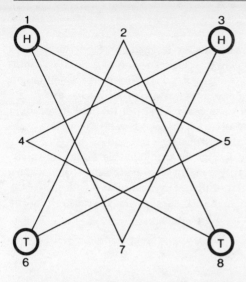

Now the object of the exercise is to move the two coins that are heads up to points 6 and 8, and the two coins that are tails up to points 1 and 3. You can only move one coin at a time and you are allowed only seven moves, although in each move you can move your coin along more than one line in succession, but it must pass directly to and from a numbered point.

Coins in a Row

(a) Take three small coins and three larger coins and lay them out in a neat row, with the small coins first.

Now, in just three moves, moving two adjacent coins at a time, you have to make a row of coins where the smaller and the larger coins *alternate*. There must be no gaps between the coins – and no cheating!

(b) This exercise can be repeated using four small coins and four larger ones, but this time you have four moves instead of three.

The Fifth Coin

This puzzle, and the next, were devised by Henry Dudeney, an eminent Victorian and a prince among puzzlers. The son of a Sussex schoolmaster and the grandson of a shepherd, Dudeney was a self-taught mathematician who loved brain-teasers above all else – excepting, perhaps, Mrs Dudeney. Between his birth in April 1857 and his death in April 1930, Dudeney invented tens of thousands of mind-bending problems and these are two of his favourites.

'Take four pennies and arrange them on the table without the assistance of another coin or any other means of measurement, so that when a fifth penny is produced it may be placed in exact contact with each of the four (without moving them) in the manner shown in the illustration. The shaded circle represents the fifth penny.

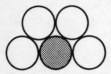

'If you trust the eye alone you will probably fail to get the four in correct position, but it can be done with absolute exactitude. How should you proceed?'

The Seventh Coin

'Lay six pennies on the table and then arrange them as shown by the six white circles in the illustration, so that if a seventh penny (the black circle) were produced it could be dropped in the centre and exactly touch each of the six.

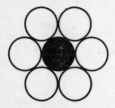

'It is required to get it exact, without any dependence on the eye. In this case you are not allowed to lift any penny off the table – otherwise there would be no puzzle at all – nor can any measuring or marking be employed. You require only six pennies.'

Head Over Heels

Take eight coins and lay them out in a circle, all heads up. Starting from any coin you like, and moving clockwise or anti-clockwise, count one, two, three, four, and turn over the fourth coin so that it is tails up. Starting again from any coin that is heads up, repeat the process. Keep at it until all the coins but one are tails up.

Odd Lines

Take twelve coins and lay them out in a very familiar pattern, so that you end up with three straight lines and an odd number of coins in each line.

Seven Rows

Take twelve coins and lay them out in seven rows, with four coins in each row.

Nine Rows

Take nineteen coins and lay them out in nine rows, with five coins in each row.

Ten Rows

Take nineteen coins and lay them out in ten rows, with five coins in each row.

Eleven Rows

Take twenty-one coins and lay them out in eleven rows, with five coins in each row.

Twelve Rows

Take twenty-one coins and lay them out in twelve rows with five coins in each row.

Fifteen Rows

Take sixteen coins and lay them out in fifteen rows, with four coins in each row.

Sixteen Rows

Take eleven coins and lay them out in sixteen rows, with three coins in each row.

Twenty-one Rows

Take twenty-two coins and lay them out in twenty-one rows, with four coins in each row.

Nine-a-Side

Take thirty-two coins and lay them out in a square so that there are nine coins on each side of the square.

(a) Now remove four coins and rearrange the remaining twenty-eight so that there are still nine coins on each side of the square.

(b) Now remove a further four coins and rearrange the remaining twenty-four so that there are still nine coins on each side of the square.

(c) Finally, remove four more coins and rearrange the twenty that are left so that you can still count nine coins on each side of the square.

Triangle One

Draw a board to play on comprising fifteen coin-sized circles exactly as the diagram for Triangle Two which follows but without the joining lines

Now place 14 coins on the 'board', leaving one space blank. The aim of the game is to remove all but one of the coins from the board. A coin moves by jumping over an adjacent coin onto an empty space. Any coin that has been jumped over can be removed from the board. There are at least six possible ways of winning the game: one is described on page 192.

Triangle Two

This is exactly the same game as the last one, except that here the moves are restricted. Coins can only jump along the diagonals and across the bottom. For example, a jump from 9 to 2 would be illegal. Otherwise the same rules apply.

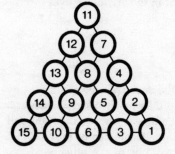

Triangle Three

This is precisely the same game as Triangle One, except that here the top position (11) must be left vacant, and the last coin must end up on that very spot.

All Change

Draw seven adjoining squares on a piece of paper, and number them from left to right. In the first three squares place three coins heads up. In the last three squares place three coins heads down. Leave the middle square empty.

The aim is to move the coins so that you end up with the three coins showing heads in squares 5, 6 and 7, and the three coins showing tails in squares 1, 2 and 3.

A move consists of sliding a coin into the adjacent empty square or jumping over an adjacent coin into the empty square.

To win the game you have to do it in fifteen moves.

Super Change

This time draw nine adjoining squares on a piece of paper. In the first four squares place four coins heads up, and in the last four squares place four coins tails up. Leave the middle square empty.

The aim is to move the coins so that you end up with the four coins showing heads in squares 6, 7, 8 and 9, and the four coins showing tails in squares 1, 2, 3 and 4.

A move consists of sliding a coin into the adjacent empty square or jumping over an adjacent coin into the empty square.

To win the game, you have to do it in twenty-four moves.

Sam Loyd's Game

This game was devised by Sam Loyd, the doyen of nineteenth century American puzzlers, and when he played the game he used pennies and nickels. In the game the pennies can be moved only to the right and down. The nickels only to the left and up. A coin can be moved to an adjacent empty square or can jump over one of the other kind. No diagonal moves are allowed. The challenge is to interchange the coins in forty-six moves.

(If you don't have pennies and nickels to hand, substitute coins can be accepted so long as you can tell the first eight from the second eight.)

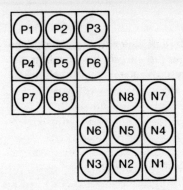

Thirty-Six

To play the game you need to draw a grid with thirty-six squares, and number them from 1–6 across the top and from A–F down one side.

Now arrange *the greatest number of coins possible* so that there is only one coin in any one square and there are not more than two coins in any horizontal, vertical or diagonal line.

Twenty-Five

Begin by drawing a grid of twenty-five squares. Next position nine coins in the central nine squares. The challenge now is to remove 8 coins and leave a ninth coin in the centre square. The removals are made by jumping one coin over another to a vacant square and removing the coin jumped. You can jump horizontally, vertically, or diagonally.

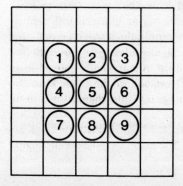

Sixteen

Draw a grid of sixteen squares and position ten coins to form an arch. Now remove all but one by jumping and removing the jumped coin. Diagonal jumps are not allowed. As the coins stand you cannot make a move, so you are allowed to transfer any single coin you wish to any vacant square before starting.

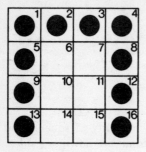

MATCHES

Three Piles

Using twenty-four matches form three piles – eleven matches in the first pile, seven in the second and six in the third.

The aim is to move matches from one pile to another so that you finish with eight matches in each pile. You may add to any pile only the same number of matches that it already contains – and all the matches must come from *one* of the other piles.

To win the game, you must do it in only three moves.

The Twelve Match Challenge

For each of these seven challenges you must begin with an arrangement of twelve matchsticks that looks like this:

1. Now move two matches and make seven squares.
2. Move three matches and leave three squares.
3. Move four matches and leave three squares.
4. Move four matches and make ten squares.
5. Remove one match, move four others and make eleven squares.
6. Remove two matches and leave two squares.
7. Remove three matches, move two others and leave three squares.

Two Dozen Matches

1. With twenty-four matches construct four squares.
2. With twenty-four matches construct five squares.
3. With twenty-four matches construct six squares.
4. With twenty-four matches construct seven squares.
5. With twenty-four matches construct nine squares.
6. With twenty-four matches construct twenty squares.
7. With twenty-four matches construct forty-two squares.
8. With twenty-four matches construct one hundred and ten squares.

The Farmer's Children

Farmer Giles lives in a beautiful farmhouse in the middle of an enormous field.

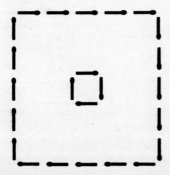

Farmer Giles has six sons and he wants to leave his land to them. How can he divide the land up equally between the six lads? (The sons aren't going to get a share of the house, by the way. That's being left on its own to Mrs Giles.)

Farmer Giles also has two daughters and Mrs Giles feels that the two daughters should share the land with the six sons. If Mrs Giles gets her way and Farmer Giles decides to leave his land (apart from the house) to all eight children, how could he divide it equally between the eight?

The Brown Boys

Farmer Brown only has five children and they are all boys.

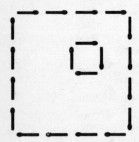

What Farmer Brown wants to leave to his five boys is his large field. He doesn't want to leave them the house that's in it.

The question is: how can Farmer Brown divide his land (apart from the house) equally among his children?

Terrific Triangles

Produce this handsome pattern with eighteen matches:

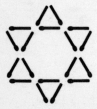

Now move two of the matches and reduce the number of triangles in the pattern from eight to six.

Terrifying Triangles

Produce this unusual pattern with thirteen matches:

Now take away three matches and leave just three triangles.

Triangular

Take nine matches and arrange them like this:

Now move three of the matches and create five triangles.

Squarely Triangular

Take eight matches and with them create two squares and four triangles.

Triangularly Triangular

Take six matches and with them create four equilateral triangles.

Small Squares

Take eight matches and form this pattern with them:

Now take away two matches and leave three squares.

Six Out of Nine

Make six squares with nine matches.

Three Out of Five

Take fifteen matches and arrange them like this:

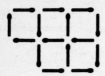

Now take away three of them and leave three squares.

Three Out of Six

Take a dozen matches and arrange them like this:

There are six equilateral triangles in the pattern. Move just four of the matches and leave a pattern of three equilateral triangles.

Roman Puzzles

The next six challenges involve Roman numerals and a maximum of twelve matches.

1. Move just one match, to make this simple sum work out:

    III − II = IV

2. Move just one match and make this simple sum work out:

    IV − II = V

3. This sum isn't so simple, but you still need move only one match to make it work out. In fact, you should be able to work out two answers to the same problem.

    VI − IV = IX

4. To make this sum work out, you must move two matches.

    VII − II = II

5. For this Roman sum you've got to *remove* three matches and nudge one to make it work out correctly.

    VII − I = V

6. And for the last Roman teaser, you don't need to touch a **single** match to make the sum work out correctly. What must you do instead?

    XI + I = X

Climbing Frame

With thirty-six matches create a pattern of thirteen squares that looks like this:

Now take away four of the matches and leave nine squares.

The Six Containers

With thirteen matches you can form a pattern that features six equal-sized containers. It will look like this:

Suppose you only have twelve matches, but you still want six equal-sized containers. How do you do it?

All Square

Take sixteen matches and use them to form this pattern:

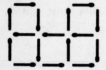

Now move three matches and create four *equal* squares.

Long Division

Take sixteen matches and form a figure that looks like this:

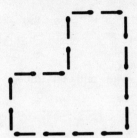

Now add eight more matches and, in doing so, *divide* the figure into four parts of equal size and shape.

Amazing

With thirty-five matches form this shape on the table:

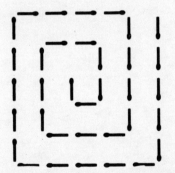

Now move four matches and create three squares.

Elevenses

With fifteen matches create eleven squares.

Ten

Place four matches vertically in a row. Add five more and make ten.

Nine

Place six matches vertically in a row. Add five more and make nine.

All You Need

With sixteen matches create four squares, like this:

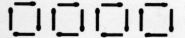

Now take away four of the matches, move three of the remaining ones and see if you can end up with whatever it is that makes the world go round.

6   SHAPES AND SIZES

All the games in this chapter need special pieces. Tangram, Octogram and Polyomino sets made of wood or plastic can be found at any good games or toy shop and in certain gift shops and large department stores. You can, of course, make the sets for yourself using thin card. For the other games in the chapter you will have to construct your own pieces, either from wood, card or even paper.

Tangram

Tangram comes from China where it is known as *'ch'i ch'ae pan'* or 'Seven-Board of Cunning'.

The Tangram set consists of seven pieces formed by the dissection of a square:

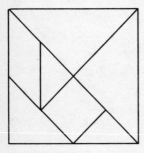

Using these seven pieces it is possible to construct an almost infinite number of amazing shapes.

As an introduction to the joys of Tangram, without referring to the diagram here, see if you can reconstruct a square. That done, attempt to create the various shapes that follow, using all seven pieces in the set for each shape. (Solutions can be found on page 201.)

The Rectangle

The Triangle

The Parallelogram

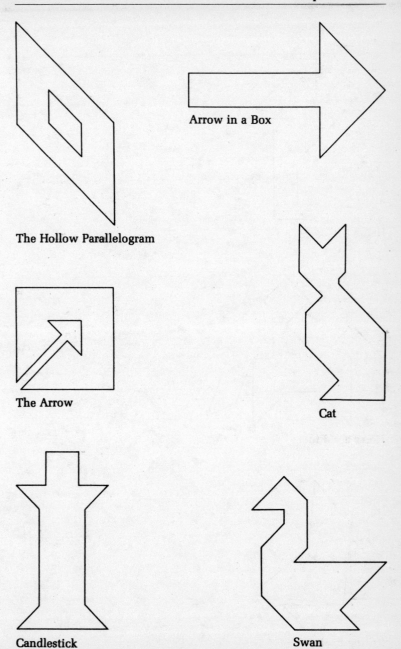

The Hollow Parallelogram

Arrow in a Box

The Arrow

Cat

Candlestick

Swan

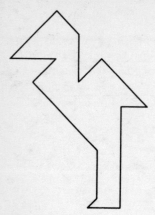

Heron

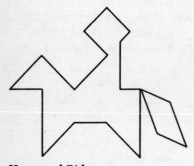

Horse and Rider

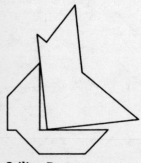

Sailing Boat

A Game of Billiards

At the turn of the century, H. E. Dudeney and Sam Loyd, the British and American masters of the art of solo entertainment, were both busy creating truly remarkable Tangram pictures. Here is Dudeney's version of a game of billiards.

You need a set of Tangram for each of the four shapes.

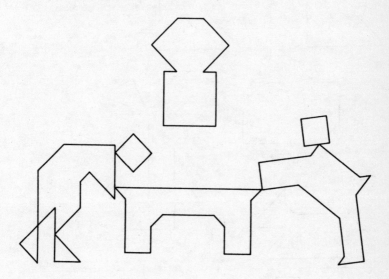

The Story of Cinderella

And with fourteen separate sets of Tangram pieces, Sam Loyd managed to retell the story of Cinderella, like this . . .

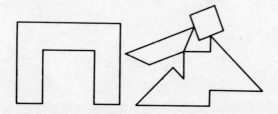

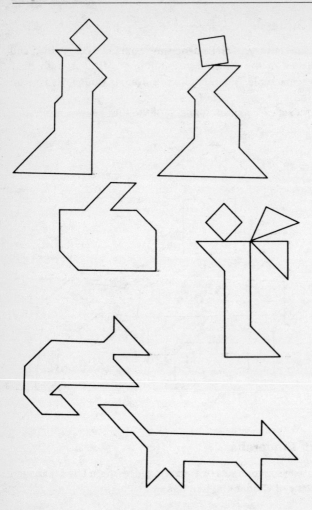

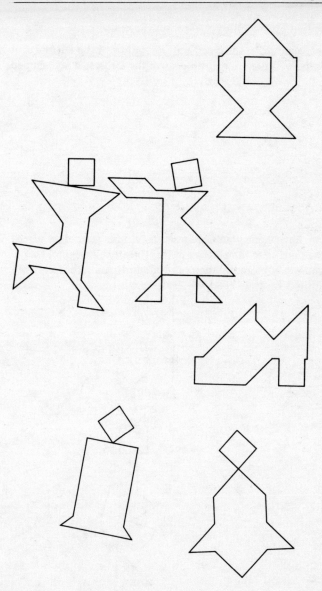

Octogram

Octogram is a modern – and Western – variation of the ancient and oriental Tangram. There are eight pieces in the Octogram set, shaped like this:

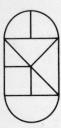

When you have made your Octogram set, shuffle your eight pieces and, without referring to the pattern, try to recreate the original shape. That done, you can be more ambitious and attempt to form the following shapes. (Solutions on page 206.)

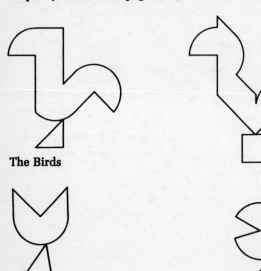

The Birds

The Cats

The Heart of the Matter

Obviously once you are equipped with a Tangram or Octogram set you need not feel confined to recreate the shapes reproduced here. You can begin to create unique Tangram and Octogram pictures of your own.

Multi-Shapes

For these you will need a pencil, ruler, scissors and thin card.

1. **Four**
   Cut this shape out four times:

Now use the four pieces to make a figure that is exactly the same shape but twice the size.

2. **Nine**
   Cut this shape out nine times:

Now use the nine pieces to make a figure that is exactly the same shape but three times as large.

3. **Sixteen**
Cut this shape out sixteen times:

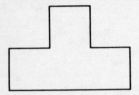

Now use the sixteen pieces to make a figure that is exactly the same shape but four times as large.
(Solutions on page 208.)

All Square

You will need a pencil, ruler, scissors and thin card.

1. **Triangular Square**
Copy this shape onto thin card and then cut up the triangle along the lines marked.

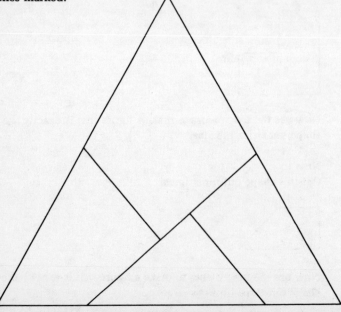

Now put the four pieces together to form a square.

2. **Cross Square**
    Copy this shape onto thin card and then cut up the cross along the
    lines marked.

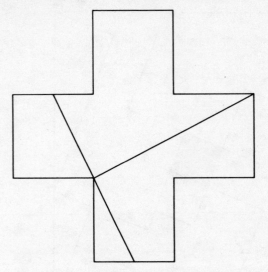

Now put the four pieces together to form a square.

3. **Rectangular Square**
    Make nine squares out of thin card to the following sizes (the
    proportions are important):

    18 × 18
    15 × 15
    14 × 14
    10 × 10
     9 × 9
     8 × 8
     7 × 7
     4 × 4
     1 × 1

    Now use these nine squares of varying size to create one rectangle
    that measures 32 × 33.

4. **Unsquare**
    Copy this shape onto thin card and then cut it up along the lines marked. Note that there is a hole in the middle.

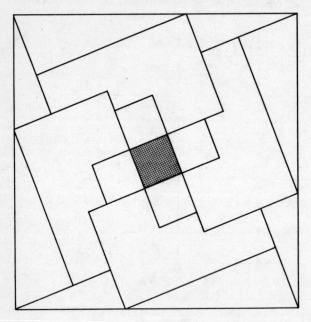

Now use the sixteen pieces to form a new square that looks exactly the same size but doesn't have a hole in the middle!
(Solutions on page 208–9.)

T for Two

Copy these shapes onto thin card and then cut them up along the lines marked. You will then have eight pieces of card. Shuffle them thoroughly and then, without referring to the book, attempt to recreate two Ts.

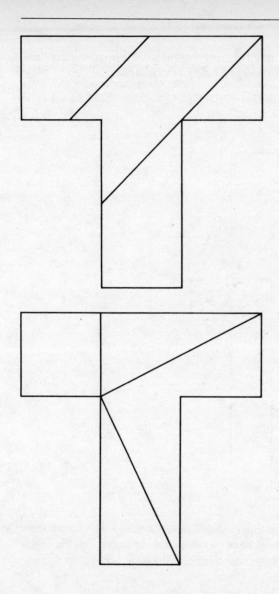

Crosses to Bear

Copy these three crosses onto thin card and then cut them up. You will then have fourteen pieces of card. Shuffle them thoroughly and then, without referring to the book, attempt to recreate the original three crosses.

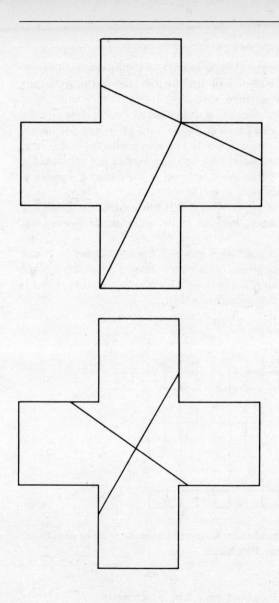

Pentominoes

Pentominoes were introduced to the world by a Californian mathematician, Solomon W. Golomb, in an article published in the *American Mathematical Monthly* in 1954.

Starting from the definition of a domino as two squares 'simply connected' (i.e. joined along their edges) he coined the word polyomino to describe the class of shapes formed by squares connected in this way. A monomino is a single square, a domino 2 squares simply connected, a tromino 3 squares, a tetromino 4 squares, a pentomino 5 squares, a hexomino 6, and so on.

From the family of polyominoes, it is the pentomino which has attracted the most interest because of its considerable recreational potential.

There are twelve distinct ways in which five squares can be joined together to form a pentomino. These twelve shapes constitute a set of pentominoes, which can either be bought from a shop or made at home. The twelve pieces in the set look like this:

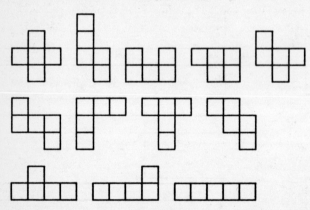

Equipped with a set of pentominoes, you can now use some or all of them to create specific shapes, like these:

1.   **Three by Five**
     Use three pentominoes to form a 3 by 5 rectangle.

2.   **Four by Five**
     Use four pentominoes to form a 4 by 5 rectangle.

3. **Five by Five**
    Use five pentominoes to form a 5 by 5 square.

4. **Five by Six**
    Use six pentominoes to form a 5 by 6 rectangle.

5. **Five by Seven**
    Use seven pentominoes to form a 5 by 7 rectangle.

6. **Four by Ten**
    Use eight pentominoes to form a 4 by 10 rectangle.

7. **Six by Ten**
    Use all twelve pentominoes to form a 6 by 10 rectangle.

8. **Five by Twelve**
    Use all twelve pentominoes to form a 5 by 12 rectangle.

9. **Four by Fifteen**
    Use all twelve pentominoes to form a 4 by 15 rectangle.

10. **Square with Hole**
    Use all twelve pentominoes to form an 8 by 8 square with a 2 by 2 hole in the centre.

11. **Square without Corners**
    Use all twelve pentominoes to form an 8 by 8 square with the four corners missing.

12. **Triplication Challenges**
    For the preceding pentomino games you will find possible solutions on pages 210–12. With the Triplication Challenge you must proceed

unaided. What you have to do here is choose one of the pieces and then use nine of the remaining eleven to construct a large-scale replica of the chosen piece. This will be three times the height and three times the length of the original. The triplication problem can be solved for each of the twelve pentominoes.

7 CALCULATOR GAMES

To attempt the calculator games and to test the 'calculator phenomena' featured in this chapter, you need to have an electronic calculator and to know how to use it. Using it is very easy:

1. Switch from OFF to ON. A zero sign will appear (you may need to press the CLEAR sign first).
2. Enter (that is, press) your first digit or number. If you are multiplying, adding, or subtracting this is the top number of the sum, if it is written down. If you are dividing this is the number you wish to divide.
3. Enter the function key you want to use.
4. Enter the other digit or number in the calculation.
5. Finally enter the equals (=) key, and the answer will appear.
6. If you make a mistake, or if you want to start another calculation, press the CLEAR key and start again.

One Thousand

For this game you will also need two dice. The aim is to reach the number 1000 – no more and no less – as quickly as possible.

Starting with your calculator set to zero, you throw the two dice. One of the dice is used to tell you which number key to press and the other tells you what operation to perform with that number, using the following key:

> 1 = add
> 2 = subtract
> 3 = multiply
> 4 = divide
> 5 = add
> 6 = multiply

You decide which die determines the number and which the operation – for example, if you throw a 3 and a 5 you may decide either to add 3 or to multiply by 5.

Continue throwing the dice, and proceed in the same manner for each throw. Try to work in whole numbers where you can, and remember that your aim is 1000 exactly. If you exceed that number you must try to get back to it by using subtraction and division.

654321

Using a calculator, two dice, pencil and paper the object of this game is to reach the number 654321 in as few turns as possible.

In each turn start by entering into the calculator any two-digit number followed by an arithmetic operator (add, subtract, multiply or divide) and then any other two-digit number. Note the result.

For example:

> 23 + 72 = 95
> or 31 × 51 = 1581

This is your first result for this turn.

Next throw the two dice. You derive a number from the dice either by adding together or multiplying the numbers shown by the dice or by using them separately to form a two-digit number. For example, if you throw a 5 and a 2, you may count this as 7, 10, 25, or 52. This is your second result for this turn.

The end result for the turn is obtained by either subtracting the second result from the first or by dividing the second into the first.

The end result may then either be added to or subtracted from your previous results.

Five-Digit Elimination

Enter a random five-digit number into the calculator. The objective is to reduce that number to zero in exactly four steps, using only the two arithmetic functions subtract and divide with any two-digit numbers.

For example:

> Number entered = 38745
>
> ÷ 45 = 861
> − 21 = 840
> ÷ 20 = 42
> − 42 = 0

Six-Digit Elimination

Enter a six-digit number into your calculator. Then proceed, as in *Five-Digit Elimination*, to reduce it to zero in exactly four steps. This is, of course, much more difficult than the previous game.

Calculator Cricket

This is a somewhat perverse form of cricket, in that the aim of the game is to be bowled out in just one over.

Enter any six-digit number into your calculator. You may not use 0 and no digit may be used twice. Now, in six goes you have to try to reduce your number to 0.

You are allowed to use any two-digit number you like in each go, and you can use any of the four mathematical functions (add, subtract, multiply, divide).

It may seem obvious to keep dividing and subtracting, but sometimes it is better to add a number in order to produce a total which can be cleanly divided by another two-digit number.

For example: imagine that you start with a six-digit number like

	583621	
Add 19	19	

	583640	
Divide by 40 =	14591	
Subtract 11 =	14580	
Divide by 45 =	324	
Divide by 12 =	27	
Subtract 27	0	Howzat!

Snakes and Ladders

In traditional Snakes and Ladders you move across the board, sometimes sliding down the snakes, at other times climbing up the ladders, and eventually arriving at the finish. With calculator Snakes and Ladders the process is exactly the same, except that instead of using a board, you use a calculator, and instead of using snakes and ladders, you use division and subtraction.

The object of the game is to reduce any number of up to six digits to 1 by either multiplying and adding, or by dividing. If you screen shows an odd number then you have to multiply; if it is even you have to divide. This is how it works:

1. If the number you enter into your calculator is an odd number you must multiply by 3 and add 1.
2. If it is an even number you must divide by 2.
3. Look at the answer and repeat the operation, multiplying the odd numbers by 3 and adding 1, and dividing the even number by 2.
4. See how many goes you will need to reduce the original six-digit number to 1.
5. Some will come down very quickly, but others which you might think should come down quickly, in fact take a lot of goes before they reach 1.

For example:
Try with a fairly small number to being with, say 35:

Odd number so multiply by 3	=	105
Add 1	=	106
Even number, so divide by 2	=	53
Odd number again so multiply by 3	=	159
Add 1	=	160
Even number so divide by 2	=	80
Even number so divide by 2	=	40
Even number so divide by 2	=	20
Even number so divide by 2	=	10
Even number so divide by 2	=	5
Odd number so multiply by 3	=	15
Add 1	=	16

Divide by 2: will produce 1 after four more goes.

Card Arithmetic

You will need a pack of cards for this game from which all the court cards are removed. Shuffle the remaining cards well and deal them face up in a straight line.

Use your calculator to help you identify groups of two or more cards whose values can be combined using the four basic arithmetic functions to equal the value of the card immediately to their right.

For example:

2 Hearts × 4 Spades = 8 Clubs

or:

10 Clubs ÷ 2 Diamonds + 4 Diamonds = 9 Spades

Remove any such group that you might identify and close up the spaces.

Continue doing this as long as you can. If you are skilful enough you will be able to get rid of all the cards in this way.

2001

Remove all the court cards from a pack of cards. Begin the game by taking any two cards from the pack and adding their values. Enter the total on to your calculator.

Now draw out two more cards. One of these will be the number you next enter into the calculator, the other will tell you whether you multiply, divide, add, or subtract with it. You can choose which card does which.

The game continues by drawing two cards at a time and increasing your total on the calculator screen. But remember that the aim is to reach 2001 in as few goes as possible.

If you find that you have used all the cards without reaching 2001 reshuffle them and carry on.

These are the mathematical functions which go with the numbered cards in the pack:

1 (ace) and 10	any function	4 and 8	÷
2 and 6	×	5 and 9	+
3 and 7	−		

For example:
Draw 6 and 4. Add them = 10
Draw 3 and 2
Either: subtract 2 (3 = −)
Or: add 3 (2 = +)

Adding is better, so add 3 = 13
Draw 10 and 6
Either: add 10 (6 = +)
Or: multiply by 6 (10 = any function)

$$13 + 10 = 23$$
$$13 \times \ \ 6 = 78$$

Multiplying is better, so multiply by 6
Carry on drawing, and make sure that you increase your total as quickly
and efficiently as you can.

Calculator Phenomena

Calculators have a wonderful way of producing unexpected numbers
from what appears to be a complete jumble of sums. The following
exercises are fascinating to do and, once you've mastered them, you can
impress your friends with these 'calculator phenomena'.

Dated Calculation

In this case, your calculator will give you an answer which not only
starts with the number you first entered into it, but which ends with the
date of the day on which you are doing the calculation.
This is how it works:

Pick any five-digit number at random and enter this into your
calculator. Multiply this by 2. Add 5. Now multiply this total by 50. Add
the date (the number of the day in the month). Add the number of days in
a year (365) an ordinary year in this case, not a leap year. Subtract 615
from the total on the calculator screen.

Look at the answer on the screen. You will see that there are seven
digits. The first five will be the five digits in your original number. The
last two will be the same as the date.

Imagine that you start with a five-digit number like: 24680

Multiply it by 2   =   49360
Add 5   =   49365
Multiply by 50   =   2468250
Add the date 21   =   2468271
Add 365   =   2468636
Subtract 615   =   2468021

The first five digits are the same as the original number, and the last two are the same as the date.

Doubling Up

Here is a set of remarkable calculator calculations which will enable you to double-up any three digit number just by performing two simple multiplication sums. When you press the equals key after the last one, the answer will flash up your original number on the screen, only this time it will be a six-digit number, with your original number appearing twice.

This is how it works:
Enter any three-digit number.
Multiply it by 11.
Multiply it by 91.
Press the equals key and look at the answer.
Your original number will appear twice in the answer.

For example:
Try it with 101   101
Multiply by 11   =   1111
Multiply by 91   =   101101

Now try it with 397   397
Multiply by 11   =   4367
Multiply by 91   =   397397

Divine Division

With this phenomenon your calculator gives you an answer to the division of any three-digit number which is the same as the number itself. All you have to do is to divide by 7, 11, and 13.

This is how you set about it:
Think of any three-digit number and enter it into your calculator.

Now make a six-digit number by entering the first three digits in the same order.
Divide this by 7.
Divide the answer by 11.
Divide this answer by 13.
Look at your answer and you'll see that it is the number you started with in the first place.

For example, imagine that you choose 572 as your number:

Enter it into your calculator		572
Make a six-digit number by repeating it	=	572572
Divide by 7	=	81796
Divide by 11	=	7436
Divide by 13	=	572

The result is the same as the number you started with: 572

Now try it yourself, using any number from 100 to 999.

Even Division

If 'divide and rule' is your motto this is a calculator phenomenon you'll enjoy. It involves eight-digit numbers that when divided by 73 and 137 invariably produce an even answer with no remainders.

There is one condition however: the eight-digit number must consist of a four-digit number repeated.

For example: Take 8531		
Repeat the four digits	=	85318531
Divide by 73	=	1168747
Now divide by 137		622763

What is even more amazing is that if your number ends with either 0 or 5, it is also possible to divide it evenly by 365 and by 50005, as well as by 73 and 137.

Try it with 4215:		
Repeat the four digits		42154215
Divide by 73	=	577455
Divide by 137	=	307695
Divide by 365	=	115491
Divide by 50005	=	843

In each case the eight-digit number can be evenly divided by these odd numbers.

Increase and Multiply

With the aid of your calculator, you can discover some of the many marvels of multiplication. For example, did you know that if you multiplied 37037 by all the numbers between 3 and 27 it would give you six-digit answers which consisted of either the same three digits repeated, or of the same digit repeated six times? Look at these:

37037	37037	37037	37037
× 3	× 4	× 5	× 6
111111	148148	185185	222222

Every time you multiply by a multiple of 3 the answer is a row of the same digits. Now carry on yourself to 27.

And did you know that if you multiplied 15873 by the multiples of 7, you would end up with answers which produced rows of the same digit? For example:

15873	15873	15873
× 7	× 14	× 21
111111	222222	333333

And when you get above 7 × 10 (= 70) the answers work like this:

$$15873 \times 77 = 1222221$$

Now try it yourself with the rest of the multiples.

Never Ending Nine

Follow these instructions and see how 9 keeps appearing at the end of your calculations, no matter how long you take in doing the sums:

Enter any number of different digits into your calculator.
Note them on a piece of paper, or in your head.
Now press the subtract sign.
Enter the same digits, but this time in their reverse order.
Note the digits in your answer.
Add the digits together.
If the total has more than one digit, add these together and you will end up with 9.

What is more, your answer to the subtraction will be a multiple of 9 as well.

Try with a small number to begin with, say 76	76
Press the subtraction sign.	
Enter the digits in their reverse order	− 67
The answer is 9	9
Now try with a larger number, say 5873	5873
Press the subtraction sign	
Enter the same digits in the reverse order	− 3785
	2088

Add the digits in the answer i.e.:

   $2 + 0 + 8 + 8 = 18$
   and $1 + 8 = 9$

And try dividing 2088 by 9 and you will see that it is a multiple of 9 as well:

   $2088 \div 9 = 232$

In Their Prime

Prime numbers are those which cannot be evenly divided by any other number. Here are the prime numbers that fall between 1 and 1000:

1	61	151	251	359	463
2	67	157	257	367	467
3	71	163	263	373	479
5	73	167	269	379	487
7	79	173	271	383	491
11	83	179	277	389	499
13	89	181	281	397	503
17	97	191	283	401	509
19	101	193	293	409	521
23	103	197	307	419	523
29	107	199	311	421	541
31	109	211	313	431	547
37	113	223	317	433	557
41	127	227	331	439	563
43	131	229	337	443	569
47	137	233	347	449	571
53	139	239	349	457	577
59	149	241	353	461	587

593	653	733	811	881	967
599	659	739	821	883	971
601	661	743	823	887	977
607	673	751	827	907	983
613	677	757	829	911	991
617	683	761	839	919	997
619	691	769	853	929	
631	701	773	857	937	
641	709	787	859	941	
643	719	797	863	947	
647	727	809	877	953	

Now here is a way of turning the remainders in any division of a prime number to advantage: with only a few simple sums you can be sure of always ending up with 3, no matter which prime number you choose. This is how it works:

Enter your prime number into the calculator.

Square it. That is, multiply it by itself.

Add 14 (a)

Divide the total by 12

You will always end up with a remainder of 3.

To check this, multiply the number to the left of the decimal by 12 as well.

This will always produce an answer which is 3 less than the first total at (a)

For example:

Try it with 829		829
Square it	=	687241
Add 14	=	687255
Divide by 12	=	57271.25
Multiply 57271 by 12	=	687252

Subtract 687252 from 687255
    The remainder is 3   3

The Talking Calculator

Divide 7734 by 10,000, turn your calculator upside down, and see what it says to you.

   Calculators can talk but their vocabulary is sadly limited owing to the fact that they only know nine letters. These are the numbers you have to enter in order to get the letters to appear:

To get B enter 8
To get E enter 3
To get G enter 6 (if you want a capital G enter 9)
To get H enter 4
To get I enter 1
To get L enter 7
To get S enter 5
To get Z enter 2

Of course you must remember to enter the numbers in reverse order to get the letters to appear right way round when you hold the calculator upside down.

These are some of the names the calculator can spell:

BESS	5538	BOBBIE	318808	LESLIE	317537
BILLIE	317718	ELSIE	31573	LILL	7717
BOB	808	LEO	0.37		

These are some common words:

BEE	338	HOE	304	SIGH	4615
BEG	638	HOSE	3504	SIZE	3215
BIB	818	I	1	SLOSH	45075
BLESS	55378	ILL	771	SOB	805
BOBBLE	378808	ISLE	3751	SOIL	7105
BOGGLE	376608	LESS	5537		
BOIL	7108	LIE	317		
BOOHOO	0.04008	LOG	607		
ELSE	3573	LOOSE	35007		
GEESE	35336	LOSE	3507		
GLEE	3376	LOSS	5507		
GOBBLE	378806	OBOE	3080		
GOES	5306	SEIZE	32135		
GOOSE	35006	SELL	7735		
GOSH	4506	SHE	345		
HE	34	SHELL	77345		
HIGH	4614	SHOE	3045		
HILL	7714	SIEGE	36315		

As a challenge, see how long a list of legitimate English words you can produce with your calculator. As a solo game it's good for a 379919.

8 PAPER AND PENCIL GAMES

All Ways

Take a long word – any long word will do – and write it in the centre of your paper. Now give yourself two minutes to build up as many other words as you can from the basic word. All the new words must in some way be related to the first word.

Here is an example using the word UMBRELLA:

```
          s
  s       q
  t       u
c o l d   a
  r       l   g
UMBRELLA  A
  a       l
  i       o
r a i n   s o a k e d
  c       h       r
  o       e       e
  d a m p s       n       f
  t               c h i l l
                  h       o
                  e       o
                  drowned
```

Alpha

This is a word-listing game in which you have a time limit of ten minutes in which to list words beginning and ending with the same letter of the alphabet.

First write the letters of the alphabet down the left-hand margin of your sheet of paper. Then for each letter find the longest possible word which begins and ends with that letter. When the time limit has expired, you score one point for each letter of each word you have listed. Your completed list might look something like this:

A	AMNESIA	=	7	G	GRADUATING	=	10
B	BEDAUB	=	6	H	HUNCH	=	5
C	CYCLONIC	=	8	I			
D	DEDICATED	=	9	J			
E	EVERYONE	=	8	K	KAYAK	=	5
F	FLUFF	=	5	L	LONGITUDINAL	=	12

M	METAMORPHISM	=	12	T	TOURNAMENT	=	9
N	NATIONALISATION	=	15	U			
O	OVERDO	=	6	V			
P	PARTNERSHIP	=	11	W	WINDOW	=	6
Q				X			
R	REGULATOR	=	9	Y	YELLOWY	=	7
S	SUCCINCTNESS	=	12	Z			

Play the game a number of times and try to improve your score. Foreign words (like uhuru) are not allowed, nor are proper names (like Xerox) or slang (like zizz).

Alphabet Story

You have fifteen minutes in which to concoct a story of exactly twenty-six words. And each word of the story, which can be punctuated as you please, must start with a successive letter of the alphabet, right the way from A to Z.

A bright concept! Don't everyone feel good hearing it just knowledgeably landed . . . ?

Anagrams

The aim of the game is to take an everyday word or phrase and use the letters in that word or phrase to create a new word or phrase – and preferably one that has some bearing on the original. For example, while it is clever to be able to transform *scythe* into *chesty*, it is both clever and witty to turn *conversation* into *voices rant on*.

Here are twenty ingenious anagrams, both to inspire you and to give you an impression of the game's potential:

desperation	a rope ends it
punishment	nine thumps
endearments	tender names
prosecutors	court posers
twinges	we sting
softheartedness	often sheds tears
therapeutics	apt is the cure

degradedness	greed's sad end
a decimal point	I'm a dot in place
the countryside	no city dust here
the nudist colony	no untidy clothes
the detectives	detect thieves
a shoplifter	has to pilfer
one hug	enough?
the eyes	they see
the Mona Lisa	no hat, a smile
gold and silver	grand old evils
circumstantial evidence	can ruin a selected victim
medical consultations	noted miscalculations
a sentence of death	faces one at the end

Arena

Give yourself fifteen minutes in which to form as long a list as possible of 5-letter words which have a vowel as the first letter, a consonant as the second, a vowel as the third, a consonant as the fourth, and a vowel as the last letter. Such a list might include words such as these:

ARENA	OPERA	UNITE
AROMA	ABODE	AMUSE
ELOPE	AWAKE	OKAPI
EVADE	IMAGE	AGATE

Play the game on different days of the week and see on which day your vocabulary appears to be at its most expansive.

Category Crosswords

Draw a crossword grid, or preferably use a blank crossword grid from a newspaper or magazine.

Now choose a category, perhaps one of the following:

COUNTRIES	BREEDS OF DOG
TOWNS AND CITIES	GIRLS' NAMES
FLOWERS	BOOK TITLES
BIRDS	SONG TITLES

ANIMALS   STATES OF THE USA
RIVERS   FOOD

The aim of the game is to fill in the crossword grid, using only words connected with your chosen category. Of course it is easy at first, but it becomes harder and harder as you have to put in words connecting with the letters of the words you have already entered.

Changelings

This was one of the most popular of all Victorian games and a favourite pastime of that remarkable don and dodo-fancier, Lewis Carroll. To play the game you must transform one word into another, changing one letter at a time and creating a new word at every stage.

Here are a few examples:
In three steps turn DOG into CAT (DOG/COG/COT/CAT)
In four steps turn BOY into MAN (BOY/TOY/TON/TAN/MAN)
In six steps turn SHIP into BOAT (SHIP/SLIP/SLAP/SLAT/SEAT/BEAT/BOAT)
In eight steps turn BLACK into WHITE (BLACK/SLACK/SHACK/SHARK/SHARE/SHIRE/SHINE/WHINE/WHITE)

To play the game all you need to do is think of two contrasting words of the same length and move from one to the other in as few steps as possible. For practice, have a go at these, devised by Lewis Carroll himself:

1. Drive PIG into STY with four links.
2. Raise FOUR to FIVE with six links.
3. Make WHEAT into BREAD with six links.
4. Touch NOSE with CHIN with five links.
5. Change TEARS into SMILE with five links.
6. Make HARE into SOUP with six links.
7. PITCH TENTS with five links.
8. Cover EYE with LID with three links.
9. Prove PITY to be GOOD with six links.
10. Turn POOR into RICH with five links.
11. Get WOOD from TREE with seven links.
12. Prove GRASS to be GREEN with seven links.
13. Evolve MAN from APE with five links.
14. Make FLOUR into BREAD with five links.

15. Change ELM into OAK with seven links.
16. Make TEA HOT with three links.
17. Get COAL from MINE with five links.
18. Change BLACK to WHITE with six links.
19. Turn WITCH into FAIRY with 12 links.
20. Make WINTER SUMMER with 13 links.

(Solutions on pages 213–14.)

Combinations

Choose a two-letter combination from the following list:

GN	DR	XD
BR	NV	DY
TC	LG	BU
PT	FT	HL
MN	WD	LM

The aim of the game is to see how many words you can think of that contain the two-letter combination. Each word must have the two letters inside it, not at the beginning or the end.

As an example, if you choose the combination DR your list could include the words . . .

HUNDRED	ADDRESS	MANDRAKE	QUADRANGLE
WONDROUS	UNDRESS	MANDRILL	PADRE

. . . and quite a few more.

Set yourself a time-limit, and when you have exhausted the two-letter combinations listed above, play the game with other combinations of your own.

Five by Five

To play the game you need to draw a large square and divide it so there are twenty-five smaller squares inside it.

Now fill the squares with letters in an attempt to create as many words as you can, both horizontally and vertically. You have ten minutes in which to think of the letters and at the end you will score 1 point for every one-letter word, 2 points for the two-letter word, 3 points for the three-letter words and so on. Here's how a completed grid might look:

```
G R A P E
R O V E R
O B E S E
P O R T S
E T T O T
```

And here's what the grid would score:

From GRAPE: GRAPE, RAPE, RAP, APE, A	16 points
From ROVER: ROVER, ROVE, OVER, ER	15 points
From OBESE: OBESE, BE	7 points
From PORTS: PORTS, PORT, PO, OR	13 points
From ETTOT: TOT, TO	5 points
From GROPE: GROPE, ROPE	9 points
From ROBOT: ROBOT, ROB	8 points
From AVERT: AVERT, AVER, ER, A	12 points
From PESTO: PEST, TO	6 points
From EREST: REST, ERE, RE	9 points

That's a total of 100, which is good, but not wonderful when you consider that 875 is the technical top mark. However, anything over 200 is impressive.

Hide and Seek

To play the game all you have to do is think of a suitably long word – like ABANDONMENT or BEAUTIFUL or CASUALTY or DUNDERHEAD or EVERGREEN or FRATERNITY or GEOGRAPHY or HOSPITALITY or IGNORANCE or JOVIALITY or KINGDOM or LONELINESS or METAMORPHOSIS or NATIVITY or OPPORTUNITY or PATRONAGE or QUICKNESS or ROTUNDITY or SERENDIPITY or TANTAMOUNT or UNDERSTANDING or VARICOSE or WEARISOME or XYLOPHONE or ZOOLOGY, to give you a choice of twenty-six – and make a list of all the words you can think of that can be formed out of the letters contained in the long word. Out of ABANDONMENT alone it is possible to create over fifty other words!

Initials

Take a couple of eight-, nine- or ten-letter words – or a couple of complete phrases so long as each phrase contains the same number of letters – and write them vertically down the left margin of the page side by side. You'll find you've created some sets of initials. All you have to do is set yourself a time limit and come up with the names to fit the initials.

Taking EVERYMAN and PLAYMATE as the words, here's an example:

E	P	– Enoch Powell (British politician)
V	L	– Valéry Larband (French novelist)
E	A	– Eric Ambler (British thriller writer)
R	Y	– Robert Young (American film star)
Y	M	– Yves Montand (French film star)
M	A	– Maxwell Anderson (American writer)
A	T	– Anthony Trollope (British novelist)
N	E	– Nellie Edwards (Gyles Brandreth's Canadian cousin)

It isn't easy (except if you cheat), so consulting reference books and dictionaries of biography is allowed.

Odd Man Out

Here is a game that appears very easy to master. Appearances can be deceptive.

In the diagram start with any circle, count 1, 2, 3 and put a dot in the third circle. Keep doing this, starting with any other circle, except the circles that have dots in them, and try to fill all the circles except one with dots. You should have six circles with dots in them when you have finished.

(If you need help, turn to page 214.)

Pencil Power

1. Draw this open envelope, in one line, without crossing or retracing a line, or lifting the pencil:

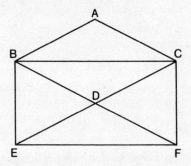

2. Draw this figure in one continuous line, without crossing a line, retracing a line, or lifting your pencil from the paper.

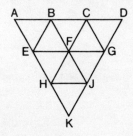

3. Draw this figure in one continuous line, without lifting the pencil from the paper, crossing a line, or retracing a line.

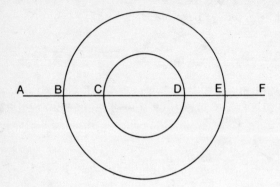

(Solution on pages 214–15.)

Pen Power

Is it possible to put nine pigs in four pens so that there is an uneven number of pigs in each of the four pens? Try to do this with pencil and paper.

(Solution on page 215.)

Round Numbers

Can you put the numbers 1, 2, 3, 4, 5, 6, into the spaces on this diagram so that the numbers on each circle add up to 14?

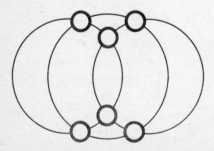

The solution is on page 215. Once you have solved this problem, try creating other similar diagrams with higher numbers but the same totals on each circle.

Scaffold

Give yourself three letters – R.D.T. for example – and ten minutes in which to form a list of words which contains those three letters in the order given. If R.D.T. were the letters given, your list might include:

    ARIDITY
    CORDIALITY
    CORDITE
    CREDIT
    GRADUATE
    INTRODUCTION
    PREDATOR
    PRODUCT
    RADIOLOGIST
    RADIATOR

The three letters should be chosen carefully so that it is possible to find a good number of words which use them. Thus L,M,E or R,F,N or M,I,T, for example, would be satisfactory, but Z,Q,N or W,X,F could just possibly result in scores of zero all round.

On different days give yourself different sets of letters, but choose them carefully. ABE and MAT, for example, will serve you well, but XYZ or OPQ would bring the game to a standstill.

Seeing Stars

If you add up any of the straight lines of numbers in this 5-pointed star, you always get the same answer, 32.

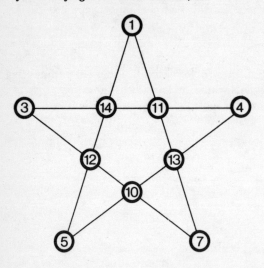

With this 6-pointed star, the total is always 27.

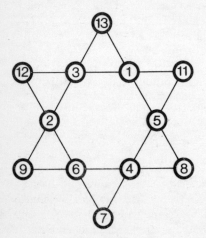

To play the game, choose any number above 32 at random and then do your best to create a five- or six-pointed star in which the numbers in each and every straight line add up to your chosen random number.

Space Filler

Choose a long word (the longer the better) and write it vertically down the left-hand side of your piece of paper. Now write the same word vertically down the right side, but this time spelling it backwards. So if the word is MUSHROOM the layout should look like this:

```
M                          M
U                          O
S                          O
H                          R
R                          H
O                          S
O                          U
M                          M
```

The aim of the game is to fill the spaces between the letters with the longest words you can find and the longer they are the better you do, because you get points for the number of letters in each word. This is what you could score with MUSHROOM:

M	INIMU	M	7 points
U	NDERG	O	7 points
S	AG	O	4 points
H	UMDINGE	R	9 points
R	EBIRT	H	7 points
O	STRICHE	S	9 points
O	RMOL	U	6 points
M	AXIMU	M	7 points Total: 56 points

Play a series of games with, say, an eight-letter word to start with, and see if you can improve your score with each game.

Stairway

Choose a letter, any letter, and then give yourself ten minutes in which to build up a verbal stairway of words beginning with that letter. The first word will have two letters, the second three, and so on. Here's where B might lead you:

B
BE
BOA
BONE
BRAND
BASKET
BRACKET
BOUNCING
BRANDRETH

All the words have to be in the dictionary (yes, Brandreth *is* there!) and the satisfaction of the game lies in producing a stairway with a large number of steps. F is a good letter to start with because it can lead you to the longest word in the *Oxford English Dictionary*:
FLOCCINAUCINIHILIPICATION.

Vowel Play

Pick a vowel and then give yourself ten minutes in which to produce a list of words which must conform to the following simple rules:
Each word must contain at least five letters.
Each word must contain the chosen vowel twice or more and must contain no other vowel.
Proper nouns, foreign words and hyphenated words are not allowed.

Starting with *aardvark* (which is allowed so long as you don't consider South African words 'foreign') and going on to *zoology* (which is allowed so long as you don't consider y to be a vowel), the game has considerable vocabulary-stretching potential.

Word Squares

For anyone fascinated by words, creating word squares is among the most absorbing of all paper and pencil pastimes. The idea is simply to form a square of different words reading the same vertically as horizontally. Squares involving three-, four- and five-letter words are relatively simple. Here's an example:

```
P L A Y
L O R E
A R E A
Y E A R
```

Devising squares with six-, seven- and eight-letter words is much more difficult, while creating squares with nine-letter words is well nigh impossible – but it can be done, if you have an incredible vocabulary and an outsize dictionary. One man who has both is my friend, Darryl Francis, perhaps the world's leading authority on word squares. This is one of his favourite nine-letter wonders:

```
F R A T E R I E S
R E G I M E N A L
A G I T A T I V E
T I T A N I T E S
E M A N A T I S T
R E T I T R A T E
I N I T I A T O R
E A V E S T O N E
S L E S T E R E D
```

What is more, Mr Francis has some 999 others in the same vein. However, when you start playing the game, it's best to stick to five- and six-letter words.

9 MENTAL GAMES

These are called mental games not because they will make you mental –
though assuredly some of them will – but because they are all to be
played in the mind. Some are cerebral, several are silly, a few could also
be played out loud or using pencil and paper, but to really rise to the
challenges of this chapter, you should attempt all the games entirely in
your head, at least in the first instance.

Fizz Buzz

All you have to do to play this game is count from one to infinity. It
sounds simple, but there is a catch. When you get to the number 5 or a
multiple of 5 (10, 15, 20, 25, 30) you must say FIZZ and when you get to 7
or a multiple of 7 (14, 21, 28) you must say BUZZ and when you get to a
multiple of 5 and 7 (35, 70, 105) you must say FIZZ-BUZZ.

Whenever you make a mistake you must start again at zero.

If you are totally alone and don't feel self-conscious talking to
yourself, you can play Fizz-Buzz out loud. However, if you are on a train
or a plane or simply walking the streets, play the game in your head
unless you are happy to attract attention.

Last and First

Choose a category – writers, rivers, cities, animals, scientists, games for
one player – and then think up a never-ending list of words that fit the
category – the catch being that the first letter of each word must be the
same as the last letter of the preceding word. For example, if the category
was countries, the words might be Australia, Austria, Aden, Norway,
Yugoslavia, Afghanistan, Nigeria, and so on. The moment you get stuck
you've lost.

Messing about in Quotes

Think of a well-known phrase or quotation or cliché and then decide
who might have said it. The aim of the game is not to discover who did
say it, but to conceive an unlikely – but amusing or ingenious – author
for the quotation. For example, who said 'Thank God it's Friday!'?
Robinson Crusoe, of course.

This is one of those games that works wonderfully if you warm to the concept, but seems entirely pointless if you don't.

Palindromes

John Taylor is credited with having created the first English palindromic sentence at the beginning of the seventeenth century:

> Lewd did I live & evil I did dwel.

Spelling habits have changed; today a more acceptable version would read:

> Evil I did dwell; lewd did I live.

Many recent palindromes involve people's names, some of them quite famous:

> Was it Eliot's toilet I saw?
> No mists reign at Tangier, St Simon!
> Sums are not set as a test on Erasmus.

Some palindromes are supposed to have been spoken by the famous. The composer Henry Purcell is said to have remarked,

> Egad, a base tone denotes a bad age!

And it is well known that the Emperor Napoleon was wont to moan during his exile:

> Able was I ere I saw Elba.

For a modern palindrome that succinctly tells a story, it would be hard to beat this one by Leigh Mercer:

> A man, a plan, a canal – Panama.

And here a half a dozen other palindromic sentences. Each one makes sense – of a sort.

> Was it a car or a cat I saw?
> Pull up if I pull up.
> Ten animals I slam in a net.
> In a regal age ran I.
> Yawn a more Roman way.
> Some men interpret nine memos.

To play the palindrome game all you have to do is think of an original palindromic sentence. If you are very clever you can make up a short palindromic story. To inspire you here is a remarkable 51-letter saga from the writer Penelope Gilliatt:

> Doc, note I dissent. A fast never prevents fatness. I diet on cod.

Pangrams

A pangram is a sentence that includes every letter of the alphabet. The best-known pangram has 33 letters:

> The quick brown fox jumps over a lazy dog.

This one has 32 letters:

> Pack my box with five dozen liquor jugs.

And this one is down to 31:

> The five boxing wizards jump quickly.

To get below 30 you have to introduce proper names. Here is one with 29:

> Quick wafting zephyrs vex bold Jim.

And here is one with just 28:

> Waltz, nymph, for quick jigs vex Bud.

No one has devised a 26-letter pangram that doesn't use names and initials or archaic words. Here is a 26-letter gem which roughly translated into everyday English means, 'Carved figures on the bank of a fjord in a rounded valley irritated an eccentric person.'

> Cwm, fjord-bank glyphs vext quiz.

To play the pangram game all you have to do is think of a 26-letter sentence that makes some sort of sense and includes the entire alphabet. For example, 'J. Q. Schwartz flung D. V. Pike my box.' Doubtless you can do better than that.

Pick a Number

To put you in an arithmetical frame of mind, here are **twenty** questions.
You must work out the answers to them in your head. **The** solutions are
on pages 215–16.

1. A certain number leaves a remainder of one when it is divided by 2,
   3, 4, 5 or 6 but leaves no remainder when it is divided by 7. What is
   the smallest possible value of the number?

2. A certain number, when divided by 2, 3, 4, 5, 6, 7, 8, 9 and 10, leaves
   remainders of 1, 2, 3, 4, 5, 6, 7, 8 and 9 respectively. What is the
   smallest possible value of the number?

3. Using each digit once and only once, form two numbers from the
   digits 1, 2, 3, 4, 5, 6, 7, 8 and 9, so that one number is twice as large as
   the other.

4. Take the numbers 1 to 10 inclusive and divide them into five pairs so
   that the sums of the respective pairs are 16, 7, 6, 17 and 9.

5. A number is composed of four digits. The last digit is two times the
   first; the second is three less than the third; the sum of the first and
   last digits is twice the third. What is the number?

6. From the digits 1 to 9 inclusive, form three numbers of three digits
   each, so that the third number is three times as great as the first, and
   the second number is equal to the third minus the first.

7. Divide the number 45 into four parts so that adding 2 to the first,
   subtracting 2 from the second, multiplying the third by 2, and
   dividing the fourth by 2 will all give the same result.

8. If a certain number is reduced by 7 and the remainder multiplied by
   7, the result will be the same as if the number were reduced by 5 and
   the remainder multiplied by 5. What is the number?

9. A certain number is the sum of five smaller numbers and is evenly
   divisible by each one of the five. What is the smallest possible value
   for the large number and what are the five small ones that add up to
   it?

10. A certain number can be divided into two numbers, one of which is
    twice as large as the other. These two smaller numbers are such that
    the difference between them is the same as the difference between
    their squares. What are the numbers?

11. A father is four times as old as his son. Twenty years from now the father will be twice as old as the son. How old are father and son today?

12. The ages of a father and his son are the same with the digits reversed. A year ago the father was twice as old as the son. How old are the father and son now?

13. The age of a man plus that of his wife is 91 years. The man is now twice as old as his wife was when he was as old as she is now. What are their ages now?

14. A brick weighs three-fourths of a brick and three-fourths of a pound. How many pounds does it weigh?

15. A collection of animals, including both beasts and birds, has 43 heads and 120 feet. How many beasts and how many birds are in the lot?

16. In a certain family that includes both boys and girls, each boy has just as many brothers as sisters, but each girl has twice as many brothers as sisters. How many boys and how many girls are in the family?

17. How many minutes per mile do you save by increasing your speed from 12 to 15 miles an hour? From 15 to 20? From 20 to 30? If you are travelling 30 miles an hour, how much must you increase your speed to save one minute per mile? If you are travelling 60 miles an hour?

18. A man drives a certain distance at 60 miles an hour and arrives one hour earlier than if he had travelled at 50 miles an hour. What is the distance?

19. If you drive a certain distance at 40 miles an hour and back at 20 miles an hour, what is your average speed for the round trip?

20. If five cats catch five mice in five minutes, how many cats will catch one mouse in one minute?

Now, still in your head, can you find a way of arranging the numbers 1 to 16 in a four-by-four square so that each line across, down and diagonally adds up to the same number?

You will find one way of doing it on page 216. There are several other possible ways, of course, (7040 of them in fact!), which is why the challenge can be counted as a game and not simply as a puzzle. J. B. Pick, one of the twentieth century's great authorities on games of every description, maintained very firmly that mathematical posers could only be called 'games' when they involved 'several possible solutions, the number of which the more determined and intellectual may seek to discover'.

Here then is the pick of Pick's mathematical games:

Marriages
Find the number of possible arrangements of x married couples seated round a table alternately man and woman, the wives being in given positions, the husbands placed in such a way that no man sits next to his wife.

Mosaics
Discover the number of ways in which it is possible to arrange four equal isosceles right-angle triangles of different colours, to form distinct designs.

One, Two, Three, Four
Using each of the digits 1, 2, 3 and 4 only once in the expression of each number, express consecutive numbers from one upwards as far as possible. Mathematicians as doggedly incompetent as myself can't progress much further than ten, but brighter luminaries with the aid of decimals, algebra, products and positive integral powers (whatever these may be) are capable of arriving at 88 and the fanatically able by employing such abstrusities as symbols for square roots, factorials, negative integral indices and fractional indices may, after a month or two, hit the mark 312. At least, so it is said.

Ring the Changes
Find as many ways as possible of arranging x people in a ring so that no one has the same neighbours more than once.

QT

The aim of the game is to compile as long a list as possible of words made up from a combination of two or more letters of the alphabet – in the way that QT make 'cutie'. Here are some examples of what is allowed:

RT spells 'arty'   IC spells 'icy'
YR spells 'wire'   IV spells 'ivy'

CT spells 'city'   KG spells 'cagey'
NV spells 'envy'   SA spells 'essay'

And here are a few that only just scrape by:

TDS spells 'tedious'   XTC spells 'ecstasy'
CQRT spells 'security'   XMN spells 'examine'
JL spells 'jail'

And here are one or two plurals:

II spells 'eyes'   TT spells 'tease'
YY spells 'wise'   EE spells 'ease'
UU spells 'use'

Radio Times

This is a supremely silly game, but it can enliven a dull car journey and provide a few smiles if you happen to be feeling solitary and sad. To play the game, you need a radio tuned to a station that features voices rather than music. Keep the radio switched *off* and then in a solemn voice ask it 'What *did* the actress say to the bishop?' – at which point turn on the radio and marvel at the aptness – or total absurdity – of the reply.

If you want to play the game more than once you should formulate a series of improbable – if not improper – questions to put to your radio and change stations once or twice during the course of the game.

Sentences

The aim of this game is to compose in your head the longest sentence that you can possibly manage in under a minute *without using a word containing more than three letters*. 'The sly spy hid my tie and if I am not to die I can but try to get it and hit him or his dog on the ear or in the eye' is the sort of sentence to attempt – and if you think it's pretty feeble, try for yourself. This is one of those games that's easier described than played.

Spelling Bee

Take 26 long and complicated but not obscure words – each one beginning with a different letter of the alphabet – and spell them to yourself.
When you have spelt them all, check in a dictionary to make sure you
have spelt them correctly. Here are the sorts of words that suit the game.

accompaniment	nasturtium
biddable	obstetrician
chrysanthemum	psittacosis
diaphanous	questionnaire
eucalyptus	ratiocinate
flibbertigibbet	somnambulistic
gherkin	teleosaurus
hibiscus	utilitarianism
irremissible	vicennial
Jeroboam	Wykehamist
kerosene	xystus
logarithmically	yashmak
mathematics	zymotic

Once you are sure you know how to spell the 26 words correctly, go
through the list again, this time spelling each word *backwards*.

Stepping Stones

In this game of word associations you have to get from A to B via X, Y and
Z. Begin by giving yourself five subjects chosen at random: say, Music
(A), Astronomy (B), Cookery (X), Finance (Y) and Cars (Z). Now in as few
steps as possible, get yourself from A to B, via X, Y and Z. For example,
here are two ways of doing it.

1. Dame Nellie Melba was an opera singer. (Music)
2. Peach Melba was named in her honour. (Cookery)
3. Every peach contains a stone.
4. A stone is fourteen pounds.
5. Pounds are Sterling. (Finance)
6. Stirling Moss was a British racing driver. (Cars)
7. Moss, so they say, is not gathered by rolling stones.
8. The Rolling Stones are rock stars.
9. Stars, in fact, are formed from gas not from rock. (Astronomy)

1. Musicians usually begin by learning scales. (Music)
2. Scales are found on fish.
3. Salmon is the fish most often served with salads. (Cookery)
4. Salmon may be caught from river banks.
5. Banks are financial institutions. (Finance)
6. Bank managers usually play golf.
7. The Golf is an imported car, unlike the Mini. (Cars)
8. Mini-skirts should only be worn by women with heavenly bodies.
9. Stars and planets are heavenly bodies. (Astronomy)

Taboo

This game sounds so simple, yet it is next to impossible to master. To play you must choose an everyday word – something obvious like 'yes' or 'no' – and give yourself a time limit – something like five or ten minutes – in which the words *must not cross* your *mind*. 'Yes' and 'no' and 'this' and 'that' are pretty difficult to avoid, but you'll find it's the words 'and' and 'I' that are well nigh impossible.

Start with ten points and lose a point every time the taboo word occurs to you. If you have any points left when your time is up, you've won.

Tongue-Twisters

Give yourself a tongue-twister and just one minute in which to repeat it as many times as possible.

'The sixth sick sheik's sixth sheep's sick' is supposed to be the most difficult one in the English language, but there are plenty of others that are simpler but almost as frustrating:

Peggy Babcock
Truly rural
Lemon liniment
Cricket critic
Preshrunk shirts
Strange strategic statistics
Twine three tree twigs
Six slim slick slender saplings
That bloke's back brake-block broke

She sells sea-shells sitting on the sea-shore.
Big Bill Billiken blew bursting bubbles by billions.
The minx mixed a medicinal mixture.
A shifty snake selling snake-skin slippers.
They threw three thick things at three thrilled thrushes.
Frisky Freddie feeds on fresh fried fish.
Sally Sloop saw six sad sheep standing on the sea-shore
    shamelessly shamming sleep.
The city sweep took his sooty sheet in the city street.
Shiver and slither shovelling slushy squelchy snow.
Whistle for the thistle sifter.
The Swiss witch which bewitched this switch wished the switch
    bewitched.

You might think this is a game that can only be played out loud. Not
so. It is quite as difficult played in the head.

Verse and Worse

The best-known limerick writer was that eminent Victorian, Edward
Lear (1812–1888):

Although at the limericks of Lear
    We may be tempted to sneer
        We should never forget
        That we owe him a debt
For his work as the first pioneer.

Of course, Lear's limericks were all remarkably respectable:

There was an old person from Twickenham
    Who whipped his four horses to quicken 'em:
        When they stood on one leg
        He said faintly 'I beg
We may go back directly to Twickenham!'

And the trouble with respectable limericks is that they can be somewhat
short on laughs:

The Limerick packs laughs anatomical
    Into space that's quite economical
        But the good ones I've seen
        So seldom are clean
And the clean ones so seldom are comical.

Now the aim of this game is to compose a limerick that is both respectable *and* funny. It's quite a challenge, but positive child's play when compared with having to write an entire poem in one sentence. This masterpiece is by John Slim. To play Slim's Game you must compose a one-sentence verse of your own that is at least as long as this:

Death Sentence

Have you heard how Cuthbert Hatch,
To find a gas leak, struck a match
And thereby hastened his despatch
To realms unknown to you and me,
Who have not yet been foolishly
Inclined to leave posterity
To puzzle for itself just why
We chose to make our fragments fly
For ever upwards to the sky,
As Cuthbert did when in the dark
He smelled a smell and sparked a spark
Which sent him rising like a lark
– A very shattered fowl, it's true,
With no lump large enough to stew
And nothing any cat could chew –
Into the unresisting space
Where there is never any place
To rest one's feet or wash one's face,
Though this, for faceless, feetless folk,
As Cuthbert was by then, poor bloke,
Is not by any means a yoke
Which is impossible to bear,
For it's with truth that I declare
That cases are extremely rare
Of people ceasing to exist
And then, assuming they'll be missed,
Proceeding forthwith to insist
On spreading sadness with their pen
Among their former fellow-men
With news of things beyond their ken
By writing letters to the Press
To say that they are in a mess
Which words in print cannot express,
For they're aware that we below
Quite rarely care just how they go
And, once they've gone, don't want to know
The finer details of the fate
Which suddenly transformed their state
From Man Alive into The Late
Lamented such as Cuthbert Hatch,

Who found that leak with lighted match
And who thereafter failed to catch
The interest of the public eye
Or stir mankind to spare a sigh
– Which may explain precisely why
I think that Cuthbert Hatch (The Late)
Would not expect to read (or rate)
A second sentence on his fate?

Word Building

Choose a key word and give yourself five minutes in which to think of
simple or compound words which incorporate the key word.

Head, heart, straight, strong, weak and water all make excellent key
words. Self is another good one:

> Self
> Selfish
> Selfless
> Self-made
> Self-destructive
> Self-confident
> Self-inflicted
> Self-conscious
> Self-righteous
> Self-seeking
> Self-sufficient
> Self-accusation
> Self-same
> Self-contained
> Self-supporting
> Self-respect
> Himself
> Herself
> Oneself
> Itself
> etc.

Keep a mental note of how many words you manage to list for each
key word. A score of 20 is good, 30 is excellent and 40 suggests you must
have consulted a dictionary.

Word Chain

Open this book – or any other – at random and look at the first word on the left-hand page. Perhaps it is 'green'. Take the last two letters of *green* and see if you can think of a word beginning with *en*. Perhaps you will choose *encircle*. Now take the last two letters of that word and do the same. Carry on making a chain like this until you can go no further. The word *tiddlywink*, for example, would bring you to a dead end, as no English word begins with *nk*.

This is how the *green* chain might continue: *green, encircle, lemon, one, never, eradicate, temper, erudite, termite, team, ambassador, orange, geranium, umbrella, lamp.* Of course, it is in your own interests not to use a word that will bring the chain to a close.

Word Order

Think of a word at random. Follow it with another word suggested by the first word, then with another suggested by the second, and so on. If the first word is 'apple', it might be followed by 'pie', 'sky', 'blue', 'colour', 'television', 'set', 'match', 'stick', 'cane', 'sugar', and so on.

After one minute you have to go into reverse gear and repeat all the words in the reverse order – from 'sugar' to 'cane' to 'stick' to 'match' to 'set' to 'television' to 'colour' to 'blue' to 'sky' to 'pie' to 'apple'.

Every time you hesitate, get the words in the wrong order or forget a word, you lose a life.

You start the game with 10 lives, and you should play ten rounds.

Word Power

Before playing the game, here is an opportunity to test your word power.

1. Is a COTYLEDON   – a leaf
                                  – a teapot
                                  – an American dance?

2. Is an EIRENICON   – an Irish statue
                                  – a loofah
                                  – a peace proposal?

3. Is a KHAMSIN
   - a blanket
   - a snow shoe
   - a wind?

4. Is a MANCHINEEL
   - a tropical fish
   - a weaver's tool
   - a tree?

5. Is a LAZZARONE
   - a pasta dish
   - a Neapolitan beggar
   - a South American lizard?

6. Is an ONAGER
   - an aphrodisiac
   - a geological fault
   - a wild ass?

7. Is a GRIFFIN
   - a novice
   - a cattle-thief
   - an African root vegetable?

8. Is a HAMMAN
   - an Indian market
   - a Chinese pastry
   - a Turkish bath?

9. Is a LAMMERGEYER
   - a Buddhist priest
   - a type of knot
   - a bird of prey?

10. Is a MAUND
   - a religious ceremony
   - a measure of weight
   - a gift of charity?

11. Is a ZEBU
   - an impure oxide of cobalt
   - a letter in the Persian alphabet
   - an ox?

12. Is TAFIA
   - a kind of grass
   - a kind of seaweed
   - a kind of rum?

13. Is a TROPHANIN
   - a type of poem
   - a rare disease
   - a poisonous drug?

14. Is a SALVIA
   - a serving dish
   - a herb
   - a breed of dog?

15. Is a PEDUNCLE — a precious stone
— an illegitimate uncle
— a stalk?

16. Is a PEKOE — a Mandarin courtier
— a Pekingese policeman
— a tea?

17. Is a PAWNEE — somebody with whom pawn is
deposited
— somebody who is given as a slave
to an Indian chief
— somebody who has broken the Islamic
Moral Law?

18. Is a PODAGRA — a kind of waterfall
— a skin complaint
— a kind of gout?

19. Is a PAYNIM — a bursar
— an apothecary
— a pagan?

The answers are on page 216.

If you scored 15 or more you have an impressive vocabulary, but if you scored rather less, don't despair. To play the game it's imagination rather than erudition that counts. What you have to do is invent a plausible-sounding word that *doesn't exist*. When thinking of the word you can devise a definition for it as well, though that is not part of the game. Once you have made up your word, look it up in the dictionary. If you find your word – with whatever definition – you've lost. Obviously the smaller the dictionary you consult, the greater your chances of success.

10   CHILDREN'S GAMES

The games and challenges in this chapter are designed to be read and enjoyed by children of almost any age, from 5 to 105.

Animal Crossbreeds

Equipment: paper and pencil

You probably know that a lion crossed with a tiger produces what people call a 'liger'. Can you make up some imaginary crossbreeds of your own? Just dream up pairs of animal names in which the last two or three letters of one name provide the first letters of the second one, and see what strange beasts you produce. Here are some examples:

> zebrat (zebra, rat)
> giraffferret (giraffe, ferret)
> antelopenguin (antelope, penguin)
> ostrichimpanzee (ostrich, chimpanzee)
> okapig (okapi, pig)

Can you concoct twenty more?

Animal Quiz

Equipment: Paper and pencil

How many names of animals do you know? Test yourself against the clock and see if you can write down an animal beginning with each letter of the alphabet in turn – and do it in two minutes. Now try again, using different animals from those on your first list, this time allowing three minutes. Still not beaten? If not, try a third list in five minutes. You may not use an animal that has appeared in the previous lists, so you will be glad of the extra thinking time.

Apple Bobbing

Equipment: Apple, bowl of water, doughnut, string

Next time you eat an apple, why not do it a little differently? Float the apple in a large bowl of water, clasp your hands behind your back, and take the first bite. You may well get a wet face, but the apple is sure to last longer.

If that has not put you off, try threading a doughnut on a string and hanging it at nose level in a doorway. You are not allowed to use your hands at all, not even for wiping the jam off your face.

Balloons in the Air

Equipment: Balloons

How long can you keep a balloon in the air just by tapping it up with one hand? Three minutes? Five? If that is too easy, see how long you can keep it up there without using your hands at all.

Card Sharp

Equipment: A pack of cards and a bucket

Stand a bucket (or waste paper basket) on the floor about 4 feet (1.25 metres) in front of you and see if you can flick a whole pack of cards into it one by one. To do it, hold each card between your first two fingers, keeping it parallel with the ground. Curve your hand round towards you, then give a strong flick with your wrist and let the card go. You may consider 40 a very good score, but can you manage all 52?

Catch in the Cup

Equipment: Paper cup, thread and a button

For this home-made version of a very old game you need a paper cup, a piece of thread about 2 feet (60 cm) long and a medium-sized button.

Make a hole in the rim of the cup and tie one end of the thread to it. Tie the button to the other end of the thread. Hold the cup at arm's length, the thread and button hanging over the side and your other hand behind your back. Now swing the button into the air and try to catch it in the cup. When you can catch it ten times out of ten it is time to make the game more difficult by using a longer piece of thread and a lighter button.

Coins in the Plate

Equipment: 10 coins and a metal plate

For this game you need ten coins and a metal plate. Put the plate on the ground and, standing 6 feet (2 metres) away, throw the coins on to it one by one. You will find it easy to hit the plate, but not at all easy to make the coins stay on it. Can you catch a whole plateful?

Coins in the Goal

Equipment: Coins and a cardboard box

Stand a small cardboard box on its side on the floor about 3 feet (1 metre) away from you. This is the goal. Now see how many coins you can roll into it. Can you manage ten out of ten? Or even twenty out of twenty?

Coins in the Water

Equipment: Coins and a bucket of water

Fill a bucket with water and drop in a small silver-coloured coin. This is the 'treasure'. The only way you can claim it as yours is to drop in another coin (preferably copper-coloured, so that you do not get confused) so that it lies directly on top of it. This is much more difficult than you think. Try to keep the bucket undisturbed for several days – or even weeks or months, if that's how long it takes – and try with more coins whenever you have any to spare. You will find this a very good way of saving! Of course, when you win the 'treasure' you are allowed to take all the other coins as well.

Concentration

Equipment: A magazine, paper and pencil

Take a page from a magazine that's got lots of words and lots of pictures on it. Look at the page for two minutes. Concentrate on it. Study it. Try to remember what's in every part of it. Now put the magazine away and make a list of as many things as you can recall seeing on that page.

When your time is up, look at the magazine again and see how much you missed.

Lists from A to Z

Equipment: Paper and pencil

You can make alphabetical lists of just about anything. Think of any subject you like – countries, cars, animals, jobs, flowers – and make an alphabetical list for each one.

Here's a start.

Countries: Argentina, Brazil, China, Denmark. . .
Cars: Austin, Bentley, Cortina, Datsun. . . .
Animals: Antelope, Bear, Cow, Dog. . . .
Jobs: Actuary, Baker, Chemist, Dentist. . . .
Flowers: Aster, Bluebell, Crocus, Daffodil. . . .

You are sure to be able to finish these lists at top speed. Think up at least another dozen subjects for yourself and see how close you can come to completing them all.

Lucky Numbers

Equipment: Paper and pencil

A quick way of working out your lucky number is to add up all the digits in your date of birth until you arrive at one single figure, e.g. if your birthdate is 24th June (6th month) 1968, add $2 + 4 + 6 + 1 + 9 + 6 + 8 = 36$. Convert 36 to a single digit by adding $3 + 6 = 9$. So 9 is your lucky number. Check this by working out the number equivalent of your name using this chart.

1	2	3	4	5	6	7	8	9
A	B	C	D	E	F	G	H	I
J	K	L	M	N	O	P	Q	R
S	T	U	V	W	X	Y	Z	

If your name is Richard Jones, you get $9 + 9 + 3 + 8 + 1 + 9 + 4 + 1 + 6 + 5 + 5 + 1 = 61$. Then $6 + 1 = 7$. If the answer to this sum had also been 9, you would have been doubly sure that 9 is your lucky number. As it is, you have the choice of 7 or 9. Make careful observations for a month to see which of the two numbers serves you better, and stick to that lucky number from then on.

Mental Pictures

Picture these problems in your mind's eye and see if you can solve them by using your imagination.

1. Imagine turning your right glove inside out and putting it on your left hand. Will the palm of the glove be against the palm of your hand or against the back of it?

2. Imagine a piece of paper with writing on one side. It has a crease right across it from the top left-hand corner to the bottom right. If you turn the paper upside down, and then turn it round with the plain side towards you, will the crease run from right to left or left to right?

3. Imagine two books side by side on a shelf. Both have pages numbered from 1–100 inclusive. If the right-hand book has been put on the shelf upside down, what number do you get if you add the page number on the extreme right of the left-hand book to that on the extreme left of the right-hand book?

4. Imagine that your sweater has a label inside the back collar. If you turn it inside out and put it on with your right arm in the left sleeve and your left arm in the right sleeve, does the label end up inside or outside and at the back or the front?

(The solutions are on page 217.)

Mirror Images

Equipment: A small mirror, paper and pencil

First try to picture in your mind which letters of the alphabet (capital letters only) still look correct when you see them in a mirror placed (a) underneath them, (b) beside them, and (c) both? Make a list of these as you think of them. Then write out the alphabet in block capitals and check your answers. Can you think of a word that would look the same if seen in the mirror from any angle?

(The answers are on page 217.)

Mirror Pictures

Equipment: A mirror, paper and pencil

Prop a mirror up against the wall and lay a sheet of paper in front of it. Now try to draw something, looking only at the mirror and not at the paper. Try a simple aeroplane, a car or an animal shape to start with and then go on to something more complicated. It is more difficult than you think.

The Nation Game

Equipment: Paper and pencil

For this game you have five minutes in which to write down all the nations you can think of. But these aren't ordinary nations like France, Australia, Germany and Greece. They are words that include the six letters 'nation', like 'donation', 'fascination' and 'consternation'.

Here are some more examples:

Carnation	Elimination
Illumination	Discrimination
Condemnation	Denomination
Impersonation	Destination
Indignation	Imagination
Examination	Termination

A score of 20 words is good, 30 is excellent and 40 or more shows remarkable determination.

Obstacle Course

Equipment: Ping-pong ball, straw, pen, newspaper and 'obstacles'

Cover a large table with newspaper and put on it a selection of 'obstacles' such as a book, small toys, ball of wool, an egg cup or any other unbreakable objects. Spread them over the table and then mark out a course on the newspaper with a felt-tipped pen. It should run from one end of the table to the other and in and out of as many items as possible. Place the ball at the start of the course and blow through the straw to start it on its way. If the ball goes off course, or falls off the table, if you knock anything over, or if you touch the ball with the straw, then back to the start you go.

If you find you can complete the course fairly easily, try it against the clock. If you have an egg-timer you could try to zoom round the course before the sand runs out.

Paper and Pencil Challenge

1. Imagine you have a strip of paper 3 cm wide and 1 metre long. You must join the ends to make a ring and then draw a pencil line along the middle of the strip all round the ring *on both sides of the paper*. But you are not allowed to lift the pencil from the paper or let the line stray from the middle and go over the edge. How do you do it?

2. Write out these letters so that they form a square:

A B C D E

F G H I J

K L M N O

P Q R S T

U V W X Y

Can you now use straight lines to join twelve letters in such a way that you draw a cross with five letters inside it and eight outside?

3. Draw a square and divide it up with four straight lines to make three rows of three squares. Now write the numbers 1 to 9 in these small squares so that they add up to fifteen (a) across the rows; (b) down the rows; (c) diagonally.

(Answers on page 217.)

Pencil Dots

Equipment: Paper and pencil

Mark on the paper a row of six dots, each 15 mm apart. Now see if you can draw lines from each dot to each of the other dots. Your pencil lines are not allowed to touch any of the intermediate dots or any of the other lines.

Pencil Maze

Equipment: Paper and pencil

Take a large sheet of paper and write on it the numbers 1 to 20, scattering them all over it. Write the same numbers a second time, again scattering them wherever you fancy. With the pencil draw a line to join both numbers 1's. Then join both 2's, then both 3's, and so on. You will have to weave a path in and out between the other numbers or other lines. You will find it more and more difficult to join the pairs as the numbers get higher. Will you have to give up before the end? What is the highest number you can reach?

Ring a Number

Equipment: Paper, pen, cardboard tube, ruler, scissors

To make this game you need a large sheet of paper, a toilet roll tube, felt-tipped pen, ruler and scissors. Cut the tube into slices to make six cardboard rings. Draw a square 'board' on the paper, made up of five rows of five squares, which should each be a little larger than the cardboard rings. Write a number between 1 and 8 in each square, the lower numbers near the middle of the board, the higher ones near the edge. Lay the paper board on the floor, stand 6 feet (2 metres) away, and throw the rings on to the board one by one. Rings can only score if they are completely inside the squares. What is your best score with six rings?

Rope Spinning

Equipment: a length of rope and a piece of string

You can have great fun trying to master this art. You need plenty of room, a piece of rope about 6 feet (2 metres) long and a great deal of time and patience. Bend back one end of the rope to make a loop just large enough for the other end to slip through loosely, and bind it back tightly with a piece of string. This small loop is called the *honda*. Thread the free end through it to make a large loop at the end of the rope. The length between this larger loop and the free end is called the *spoke*.

The 'flat' spin is the most common form of rope spinning. A loop is spun parallel with the ground, while the hand holding the spoke makes smaller concentric circles above the loop. To start the spin, hold the spoke in both hands, the right hand nearest the honda. At the same time, hold the top of the loop in both hands, the right hand once more nearest the honda. Lean forward and bring your right hand smartly across in front of your body to start making a small circle in an anticlockwise direction. At the same time the left hand goes out away from the body and round in a clockwise direction, ending near the right elbow. As you do this, drop the loop but keep hold of the spoke in both hands. Keep the right hand circling so that the spoke pushes the honda round and the loop spins above the ground. The more quickly your hand circles, the larger the loop will become.

Once you have mastered the flat spin you could try jumping in and out of the loop, or jumping in and gradually raising the loop up and over your head. Or you could gradually alter the angle of your wrist so as to make the loop spin vertically instead of horizontally. But none of this will be possible without a great deal of practice.

Skipping Marathon

Equipment: Skipping rope

You probably find skipping easy, but have you ever tried an endurance marathon? What is your record for all these different variations?

1. Skipping on to alternate feet, both on the spot and while running along.
2. One ordinary skip alternating with one skip with the arms crossed.

3. Doubles (jumping both feet together, the rope passing under the feet twice for each jump).
4. Three singles, two doubles, one treble (rope under the feet three times during one jump), three singles, two doubles, one treble . . . and so on.
5. Try all of these variations turning the rope backwards.

Soccer Match

Equipment: Paper and pencil

With this game all you have to do is make up football teams – each one manned by rather unexpected players. The idea is to form teams made up from certain categories of people, so you can play matches like these:

The Composers	v	the Pop Singers
The Statesmen	v	the Cricketers
The TV stars	v	the Scientists
The Painters	v	the Racing Drivers
The Writers	v	the Comedians

Here are the last two teams in position for the kick-off:

William
Shakespeare

John   Enid
Keats   Blyton

Agatha   Conan   A. A.
Christie   Doyle   Milne

Gyles   Charles   Emily   Rudyard   Beatrix
Brandreth Dickens   Bronte   Kipling   Potter

●

Charlie   Les   Buster   Benny   Frankie
Chaplin   Dawson   Keaton   Hill   Howerd

Harold   Stan   Oliver
Lloyd   Laurel   Hardy

Eric   Ernie
Morecambe   Wise

Bob
Hope

Spillikins

Equipment: Coloured drinking straws

Try this variation of the game of Spillikins using a packet of coloured plastic drinking straws. Begin by removing all but one of the red straws. Then write down a score for each colour: red 25 perhaps, green 10, yellow 6, blue 2, or any other variations depending on the colours of your straws. Hold all the straws upright in one hand about 15 cm above a table and let them drop. You must now pick them up one at a time without making any of the others move as you do so. If any straw moves (apart from the one you are picking up) you must start again. When you have picked up the red straw you may use it to lift or flick the one you want to pick up so that it flies up away from the others. Alternatively, you may use it to roll the other one along the table to be picked up more easily.

At the end of each turn, before you start again, add up your score according to the colours of the straws (but not including the value of the one you were trying to pick up when you were 'out'). What is your record? Can you clear the table?

Straw Darts

Equipment: Straws, paper, scissors

Make four cuts 3 inches (8 cm) long down the length of a straw, spacing them evenly round the circular end. Cut two strips of stiff paper, 5 inches (13 cm) long and 1½ inches (4 cm) wide and fold each of them in half, short sides together. Take one of the folded strips of paper, fit the fold itself inside the straw between two of the slits so that the ends stick out to make stabilisers. Fit the other paper strip into the other two slits in the same way. You now have a straw dart.

Make several more in the same way, but use longer and shorter slits, longer and shorter, wider and narrower pieces of paper so that no two darts are exactly the same. See how far each of them will fly with just a flick of the wrist. Then, using the champion, see what distance you can achieve as its all-time record.

String Games

Equipment: String

1. Cats' cradle
Take a piece of string about 3 feet (1 metre) long; tie the ends firmly in a reef knot. Slip the string over your left hand so that it passes behind your thumb, in front of three fingers, and behind your little finger. Loop the string over your right hand in the same way and pull it taut. You are now holding it with your thumbs and little fingers. Put your right index finger under the loop that goes across your left palm and draw your hands apart so that the string is taut. Repeat this with your left index finger under the loop across the right palm. This is the basic cats' cradle.

2. Fish spear
Start by holding the string with your two thumbs and little fingers as described above. Pick up the loop across your left palm with your right index finger, but as you draw your hands apart twist that index finger anti-clockwise – down towards you and up away from you – so as to twist the loop you are picking up. Pull the string taut and then drop the loop on your right thumb and also the one on your right little finger. When you pull the string taut you will have made a string version of the three-pronged fish spear used by American Indians.

3. Shooting fish spear
Make the basic cats' cradle shape. Letting the string go slack, bring your hands close together and pass the loop from your left index finger over the right index finger and its loop. Pick up the original loop on the right index finger and put it on the left. Draw the hands apart. Now drop the loop on your right index finger and the spear will fly to the left. Pick it up again. (To do this, bend the right index finger down between the two loops on the right hand and bring it up in the middle of the loop in front of the left index finger.) Now drop the loop on the left index finger and the spear will fly to the right. See how fast you can make it shoot to and fro.

4. Bird
For this shape use a piece of string 5 feet (1.5 metres) long. Start with the basic cats' cradle. Loop the little finger string under a doorknob or door handle and pull it a little to make a longer loop. Bend the little fingers towards you, over their own loop and under the side nearest them of the index finger loops, picking them up. Straighten the fingers. Pass the

little fingers under the far loop held by the door knob so that it slips over them. Pick up the near side of the thumb loop with your mouth. Bend your thumbs away from you, over the other side of their own loop and under the side nearest them of the index finger loops. Straighten up the thumbs. Then pass each of them under the loop you are holding in your mouth, which you may then release. Slip the loops off your index fingers and pull the string taut. Turn the palms of your hands to face each other, and then down to face the floor, to face each other, to face the floor. . . . The loop under the doorknob is the bird's tail and the strings imitate the wings as it flies along.

Timed Minute

Equipment: A watch

If you have a watch with a second hand on it you can try this surprisingly difficult trick of timing a minute exactly – with your eyes shut. First, wait for what *seems* like a minute before opening your eyes and checking the result. Then try counting the 60 seconds and see if that helps. Some people think it helps to count like this, for the extra numbers, they say, make the right gaps between the seconds: 'One two three four five, *two* two three four five, *three* two three four five. . .' etc. See if you can devise a method for yourself that really works.

Timed Walk

Equipment: A watch

You have two minutes in which to walk to the other side of the room. Does that sound too easy? Here is the difficult part. Just as you may take no longer than the two minutes you may not take any less time either. It must be two minutes exactly. Look at your watch when you start and as you finish. If you don't manage it exactly you must pay a penalty, which is – do it again. Every time you fail you must try again. It could take you all day just to walk across the room.

Twenty Questions

Equipment: Quick wits

Finally here are a score of brainteasing challenges, designed to test the intelligence and mental agility of solo game players of all ages.

1. In this series what are the four missing letters:

H	A	P	O	T	R
H	A	P	O	T	
T	T	W	T	M	G
—	—	—	—		

2. A man had four strapping sons. When he died, his oldest son was four years older than the second son, who was four years older than the third son, who was four years older than the youngest son, who was half the age of the eldest. How old were the four sons?

3. Add just one more letter of the alphabet to these five and you'll be able to make two everyday English words:

    Y T C E H

    What's the missing letter and what are the two English words?

4. If you want to divide 4,700 gob-stoppers between Tom, Dick and Harry, so that Tom would get 1,000 more gob-stoppers than Dick, and so that Dick would get 800 more gob-stoppers than Harry, how many gob-stoppers would you give to each boy?

5. Farmer Giles said to Farmer Brown, 'If you sell me seven acres of your land, I'll own twice as much land as you.' But Farmer Brown said to Farmer Giles, 'If you sell me seven acres of your land, I'll have just as much land as you.' How much land did each farmer have?

6. If you save 1p on January the first, 2p on January the second, 4p on January the third, 8p on January the fourth – and so on, each day doubling what you have saved the day before – how much will you have saved in all by January the thirty-first?

7. What's the difference between six dozen dozen and a half dozen dozen.

8. Can you think of a six-letter word that begins with the letter H, ends with the letter N and contains six other words within its spelling?

9. Take the letters in the words ROAST MULES and turn them – head-over-heels if necessary – into one different word.

10. Re-arrange the letters OOUSWTDNEJR to spell just one word.

11. Mr Dent drives a certain distance at 60 mph and arrives one hour earlier than if he had driven the same distance at 50 mph. How far did he travel?

12. Jack keeps eighteen red and eighteen white socks in his bottom drawer. When the lights are out and Jack can't see what he's doing, how many socks does he have to take out of the drawer to be sure of having one matching pair?

13. What do these six words have in common?

CALMNESS
CANOPY
DEFT
FIRST
SIGHTING
STUN

14. There is a word you'd use to describe something someone said to you that wasn't very nice and was certainly unflattering. It's a word that contains the five vowels – A, E, I, O and U – in their reverse order – U, O, I, E and A. Can you guess what it is?

15. Sally Ann is thirteen. Her father is forty. How many years ago was Sally Ann's father four times as old as Sally Ann?

16. What are the next two letters in this series:

D E J A F E M A A P M A
J U J U — — ?

17. If a quarter of 40 were 6, what would a third of 20 be?

18. If you see a clock reflected in a mirror and the time appears to be 2.30, what time is it really?

19. This is a sum you must do in your head.

Take a million
Divide it by four
Divide the result by five
Now divide the result by two
Divide this result by twenty
Take away fifty
Divide the result by three
Now divide the result by eight
Take away one
Divide the result by seven
Add two
Divide the result by three
Add another two
Divide the result by five.

What are you left with?

20. What could these jumbled letters mean: YES GRAND BELT HR? (You'll find the answer on the cover on the book – as well, of course, on pages 217–18.)

SOLUTIONS

BOARD GAMES

Queen's Question
Five. Referring to the diagram on p. 30, the positions are as follows:
1E, 4A, 5H, 7G, 8D.

Roving Rook
Sixteen. Referring to the diagram on p. 30, start on square 4E, move to
4A, move to 8A, move to 8H, move to 1H, move to 1A, move to 7A, move
to 7G, move to 2G, move to 2B, move to 6B, move to 6F, move to 3F, move
to 3C, move to 5C, move to 5E, to 4E. The trick is to start with the longest
move possible covering four squares not three.

Chess Routes
48,639

The simplest method of obtaining the results is to draw a chessboard and
write inside each square the number of ways or routes there are of
reaching it from the top left-hand square. Here is a start:

1	1	1	1	1	1	1	1
1	3	5	7	9	11	13	15
1	5	13	25	41	61	...	

Finish the 'board' by filling in all the numbers and find the number for
any square by adding three numbers – the number to the left of it, the
number diagonally to the left and above, and the number above it.

Jumpers
Using the figure references to the diagram on p. 30, the moves are as
follows:

1.	7A to 5C	9.	3G to 5E	17.	2H to 5E
2.	4B to 6D	10.	8B to 4F	18.	7G to 4D
3.	7E to 5C	11.	5G to 3E	19.	3E to 3C
4.	8F to 4B	12.	2D to 4F	20.	1E to 4B
5.	5A to 3C	13.	1C to 5G	21.	3A to 5C
6.	2B to 4D	14.	4H to 6F	22.	2F to 6B
7.	1A to 5E	15.	8D to 5G	23.	1G to 7A
8.	7C to 4F	16.	6H to 4F		

Eight Queens
Again using the diagram on p. 30 for reference, the queens are placed
on the following squares:
1F, 2D, 3G, 4A, 5C, 6E, 7B, 8H

The Fifteenth Man
Referring to the diagram on p. 30 place the extra man on square 4B.

1.	5A to 3C	6.	8B to 4F	11.	2H to 5E
2.	1E to 4B	7.	1C to 5G	12.	8H to 4D
3.	3A to 5C	8.	4H to 6F	13.	1G to 5C
4.	7A to 4D	9.	8D to 5G	14.	8F to 4B
5.	1A to 5E	10.	6H to 4F		

Five and Three
The smallest disc is numbered 1, the next smallest 2, and so on up to the largest which is 5. '1B' means 'move disc 1 to spike B', and so on. You can solve the puzzle in the smallest number of moves as follows:

1B, 2C, 1C, 3B, 1A, 2B, 1B, 4C, 1C, 2A, 1A, 3C, 1B, 2C, 1C, 5B, 1A, 2B, 1B, 3A, 1C, 2A, 1A, 4B, 1B, 2C, 1C, 3B, 1A, 2B, 1B.

This moves all the discs from pile A to pile B.

Lucky for Some
You need at least 44 moves. Pick up each top one by one in the following order and put each one down in the only available space, which will be either next to it or reached by jumping over one other top: 12–1–3–2–13–11–1–3–2–5–7– 9–10–8–6–4–5–7– 9–10–8–6–4–5–7– 9–10–8–6–4–3–2–12–11–2–1–2

Sam Loyd's Boxes
1. Sam Loyd writes: 'The original problem is impossible to solve except by such skullduggery as turning the 6 and 9 blocks upside down. One of the puzzle's peculiarities is that any such interchange involving two blocks immediately converts the puzzle to a solvable one. In fact, any odd number of interchanges has the same effect, whereas an even number leaves the puzzle unsolvable as before.'

2. 44 moves are required to get the vacant square in the top left-hand corner: 14, 11, 12, 8, 7, 6, 10, 12, 8, 7, 4, 3, 6, 4, 7, 14, 11, 15, 13, 9, 12, 8, 4, 10, 8, 4, 14, 11, 15, 13, 9, 12, 4, 8, 5, 4, 8, 9, 13, 14, 10, 6, 2, 1.

3. 39 moves are required to solve the third problem: 14, 15, 10, 6, 7, 11, 15, 10, 13, 9, 5, 1, 2, 3, 4, 8, 12, 15, 10, 13, 9, 5, 1, 2, 3, 4, 8, 12, 15, 14, 13, 9, 5, 1, 2, 3, 4, 8, 12.

4. The magic square can be produced in fifty moves: 12, 8, 4, 3, 2, 6, 10, 9, 13, 15, 14, 12, 8, 4, 7, 10, 9, 14, 12, 8, 4, 7, 10, 9, 6, 2, 3, 10, 9, 6, 5, 1, 2, 3, 6, 5, 3, 2, 1, 13, 14, 3, 2, 1, 13, 14, 3, 12, 15, 3.

5. This puzzle can be solved in 23 moves – the fewest possible. Move the blocks in the following order: A, B, F, E, C, A, B, F, E, C, A, B, D, H, G, A, B, D, H, G, D, E, F

6. A solution in the fewest possible moves depends entirely on the selection of the most accommodating word. Apart from the word condition the blocks themselves can be changed from horizontal to vertical order in twelve moves, the fewest possible. Therefore, when we find that by writing in the word INTERPRETING we can do what is required in twelve moves, we know that that solution cannot be beaten.

The Cross

English board: 10 to 4; 24 to 10; 15 to 17; 17 to 5; 19 to 17; 4 to 10: 10 to 24; 29 to 17

French board: 12 to 2; 26 to 12; 17 to 19; 19 to 6; 21 to 19; 2 to 12; 12 to 26; 32 to 19

The Octagon

27 to 37; 31 to 33; 37 to 27; 20 to 33; 22 to 20; 19 to 32; 33 to 31; 30 to 32; 36 to 26; 17 to 30; 26 to 24; 30 to 17; 34 to 21; 21 to 19; 18 to 20; 16 to 18; 8 to 21; 21 to 19; 7 to 20; 11 to 25; 20 to 18; 25 to 11; 11 to 13; 2 to 12; 13 to 11; 10 to 12; 4 to 6; 6 to 19

The Corsair

35 to 37; 26 to 36; 25 to 35; 23 to 25; 34 to 32; 20 to 33; 37 to 27; 7 to 20; 20 to 33; 18 to 31; 35 to 25; 5 to 18; 18 to 31; 29 to 27; 22 to 20; 15 to 13; 16 to 18; 9 to 11; 20 to 7; 7 to 5; 4 to 6; 18 to 5; 1 to 11; 33 to 20; 20 to 18; 18 to 5; 5 to 7; 36 to 26; 30 to 32; 32 to 19; 19 to 6; 2 to 12; 8 to 6; 12 to 2; 3 to 1

The World

32 to 19; 30 to 32; 17 to 30; 28 to 26; 25 to 27; 14 to 28; 34 to 21; 32 to 34; 4 to 17; 6 to 4; 18 to 5; 13 to 11; 5 to 18; 27 to 13; 7 to 20

The Apostles

32 to 19; 28 to 26; 37 to 27; 35 to 37; 25 to 35; 27 to 25; 24 to 26; 11 to 25; 25 to 27; 16 to 18; 19 to 17; 6 to 19; 4 to 6; 17 to 4; 2 to 12; 8 to 6; 2 to 7; 6 to 8; 22 to 20; 15 to 13; 12 to 14; 27 to 13; 13 to 15

The letter 'E'

32 to 19; 34 to 32; 20 to 33; 29 to 27; 33 to 20; 36 to 26; 30 to 32; 26 to 36; 18 to 31; 20 to 18; 7 to 20; 15 to 13; 20 to 7; 22 to 20; 6 to 19; 4 to 6; 18 to 5; 23 to 25; 16 to 17; 9 to 11; 2 to 12; 8 to 6; 12 to 2.

DOMINO CHALLENGES

First Square

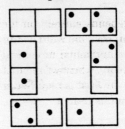

First Rectangle

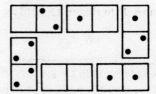

Giant Square

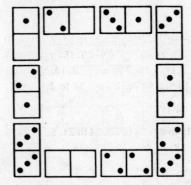

The Three Rectangles

The Five Lines

0/0 − 0/4 − 4/4
0/1 − 1/4 − 4/2
1/1 − 1/3 − 3/3
1/2 − 2/2 − 2/3
2/0 − 0/3 − 3/4

The Seven Lines

5/5 − 5/0 − 0/0
0/1 − 1/4 − 4/5
0/2 − 2/4 − 4/3
1/1 − 1/5 − 5/2
2/1 − 1/3 − 3/5
2/2 − 2/3 − 3/3
3/0 − 0/4 − 4/4

Three More Rectangles

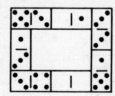 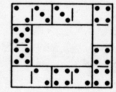

The Seven Squares

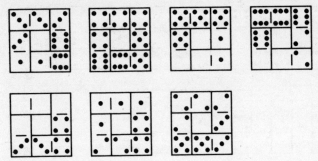

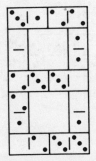

The Two Lines

2/3 − 3/3 − 3/0 − 0/0 − 0/1
3/1 − 1/1 − 1/2 − 2/2 − 2/0

Another Three Rectangles

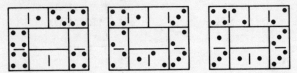

The Three Lines

2/2 − 2/3 − 3/5 − 5/0 − 0/3 − 3/3 − 3/1
4/0 − 0/2 − 2/1 − 1/5 − 5/2 − 2/4 − 4/3
0/0 − 0/1 − 1/1 − 1/4 − 4/4 − 4/5 − 5/5

The Giant Eight

Another Seven Squares

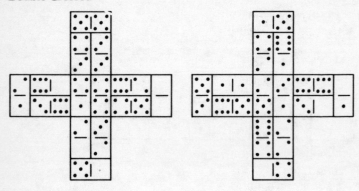

Double-Crossed

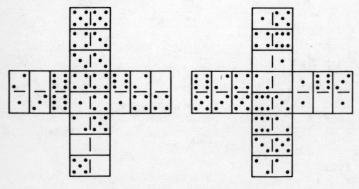

Double-Crossed Again

The Arches

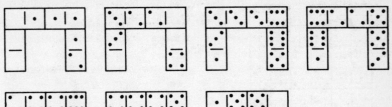

The Heptagon

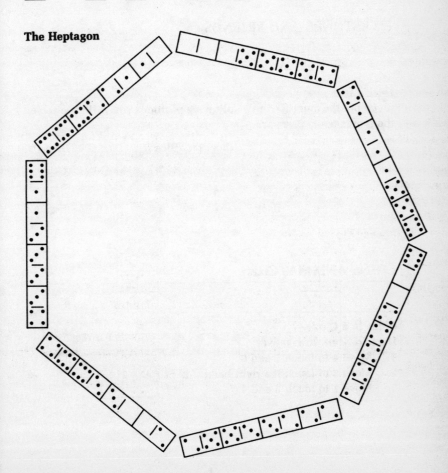

The Magic Square

FIVESTONES AND FRIENDS

Devil's Dice

If you put the four dice in the following positions you will have solved the problem.

	Dice A	Dice B	Dice C	Dice D
Viewed from Top	4	2	3	1
Front	1	4	2	3
Underneath	3	1	2	4
Back	4	3	1	2

COINS AND MATCHES

Coins in a Circle

Here are your three moves:

1. Move 4 to touch 5 and 6
2. Move 5 to touch the right hand side of 1 and 2
3. Move 1 to touch 5 and 4

Coins in a Pyramid

Here are your three moves:

1. Move 1 to below the bottom row and place it between and under 8 and 9
2. Move 7 up two rows and place it to the left of 2.
3. Move 10 up two rows and place it to the right of 3.

The H Problem

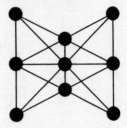

Sixteen Coins

Put your first and second fingers on the two asterisked coins and bring them round into the positions indicated by the dotted lines:

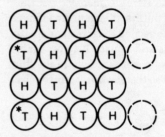

Now, with your fingers still on the same two coins, push the six coins (that is the three coins in the second row and the three coins in the bottom row) to the left and you will end up with the columns looking just as you want them.

Star Trek

Here are your seven moves:

1. Move 1 to 5
2. Move 3 to 7 to 1
3. Move 8 to 4 to 3 to 7
4. Move 6 to 2 to 8 to 4 to 3
5. Move 5 to 6 to 2 to 8
6. Move 1 to 5 to 6
7. Move 7 to 1

Coins in a Row

(a) Here are your three moves:
   1. Move coins 1 and 2 to the right of 6
   2. Move coins 6 and 1 to the right of 2
   3. Move coins 3 and 4 to the right of 5

(b) Here are your four moves:
   1. Move coins 6 and 7 to the left of 1
   2. Move coins 3 and 4 to the right of 5
   3. Move coins 7 and 1 to the right of 2
   4. Move coins 4 and 8 to the right of 6

The Fifth Coin

Here, in his own words, is the solution to Henry Dudeney's puzzle:
'First place the four pennies together as in the first diagram; then remove number 1 to the new position shown in the second diagram; and finally, carefully withdraw number 4 downwards and replace it above against numbers 2 and 3. Then they will be in the position shown in the third diagram and the fifth penny may be added so that it will exactly touch all four.

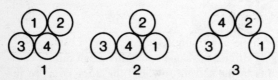

'A glance at the last diagram will show how difficult it is to judge by the eye alone the correct distance from number 1 to number 3. One is almost certain to place them too near together.'

The Seventh Coin
First arrange the pennies as in the first diagram.

Then carefully shift 6 into the position shown in the second diagram.

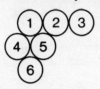

Next place 5 against 2 and 3 to get to the position in the third diagram. Number 3 can now be placed in the position indicated by the dotted circle, and a seventh penny dropped into the centre to fit exactly.

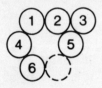

Head over Heels
Count always in the same direction, missing out one coin each time before starting the next count.

Odd Lines
Place the coins in the shape of a triangle with 5 coins on each side.

Seven Rows

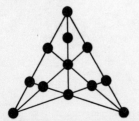

Nine Rows

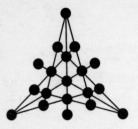

Ten Rows

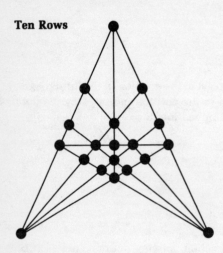

Eleven Rows

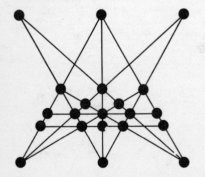

Twelve Rows

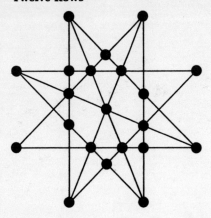

Fifteen Rows

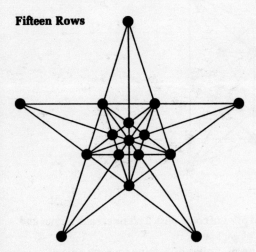

Sixteen Rows

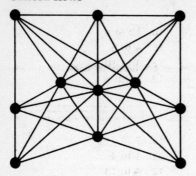

Twenty-One Rows

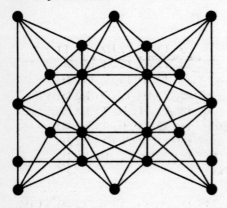

Nine-a-Side
(a) Make a 3 × 3 square of piles of coins with 2 coins at each corner and 5 coins in the centre of each side.
(b) This square is made up of 3 piles of 3 coins on each side.
(c) At each of the four corners of the square there are 4 coins and in the centre of each of the four sides there is 1 coin.

Triangle One
Leave 13 blank

1. 4 to 13	6. 7 to 2	10. 1. to 4
2. 3 to 8	7. 11 to 13	11. 4 to 13
3. 1 to 4	8. 14 to 12	12. 12 to 14
4. 10 to 3	9. 6 to 1	13. 15 to 13
5. 13 to 6		

Triangle Two
Leave 6 blank

1. 4 to 6
2. 11 to 4
3. 12 to 5
4. 2 to 7
5. 6 to 4
6. 7 to 2
7. 1 to 4
8. 10 to 8
9. 14 to 12
10. 12 to 5
11. 4 to 6
12. 3 to 10
13. 15 to 6

Triangle Three

1. 13 to 11
2. 4 to 13
3. 11 to 4
4. 10 to 8
5. 3 to 10
6. 15 to 6
7. 14 to 12
8. 2 to 7
9. 6 to 4
10. 7 to 2
11. 1 to 4
12. 4 to 13
13. 13 to 11

All Change

1. H1 H2 H3 . T3 T2 T1
2. H1 H2 . H3 T3 T2 T1
3. H1 H2 T3 H3 . T2 T1
4. H1 H2 T3 H3 T2 . T1
5. H1 H2 T3 . T2 H3 T1
6. H1 . T3 H2 T2 H3 T1
7. . H1 T3 H2 T2 H3 T1
8. T3 H1 . H2 T2 H3 T1
9. T3 H1 T2 H2 . H3 T1
10. T3 H1 T2 H2 T1 H3 .
11. T3 H1 T2 H2 T1 . H3
12. T3 H1 T2 . T1 H2 H1
13. T3 . T2 H1 T1 H2 H3
14. T3 T2 . H1 T1 H2 H3
15. T3 T2 T1 H1 . H2 H3
16. T3 T2 T1 . H1 H2 H3

Super Change

1. H1 H2 H3 H4 . T4 T3 T2 T1
2. H1 H2 H3 . H4 T4 T3 T2 T1
3. H1 H2 H3 T4 H4 . T3 T2 T1
4. H1 H2 H3 T4 H4 T3 . T2 T1
5. H1 H2 H3 T4 . T3 H4 T2 T1
6. H1 H2 . T4 H3 T3 H4 T2 T1
7. H1 . H2 T4 H3 T3 H4 T2 T1
8. H1 T4 H2 . H3 T3 H4 T2 T1
9. HL T4 H2 T3 H3 . H4 T2 T1
10. H1 T4 H2 T3 H3 T2 H4 . T1
11. H1 T4 H2 T3 H3 T2 H4 T1 .
12. H1 T4 H2 T3 H3 T2 . T1 H4
13. H1 T4 H2 T3 . T2 H3 T1 H4
14. H1 T4 . T3 H2 T2 H3 T1 H4
15. . T4 H1 T3 H2 T2 H3 T1 H4
16. T4 . T3 H1 H2 T2 H3 T1 H4
17. T4 T3 H1 . H2 T2 H3 T1 H4
18. T4 T3 H1 T2 H2 . H3 T1 H4
19. T4 T3 H1 T2 H2 T1 H3 . H4
20. T4 T3 H1 T2 H2 T1 . H3 H4
21. T4 T3 H1 T2 . T1 H2 H3 H4
22. T4 T3 . T2 H1 T1 H2 H3 H4
23. T4 T3 T2 . H1 T1 H2 H3 H4
24. T4 T3 T2 T1 H1 . H2 H3 H4
25. T4 T3 T2 T1 . H1 H2 H3 H4

Sam Loyd's Game

1. N-8 to cell 9	17. P-3 to cell 12	32. N-7 to cell 4
2. P-8 to cell 10	18. P-5 to cell 6	33. N-4 to cell 7
3. P-7 to cell 8	19. N-3 to cell 5	34. N-5 to cell 9
4. N-8 to cell 7	20. P-2 to cell 8	35. P-2 to cell 10
5. N-6 to cell 9	21. P-1 to cell 2	36. P-1 to cell 8
6. P-6 to cell 12	22. N-8 to cell 1	37. N-6 to cell 2
7. P-3 to cell 6	23. N-7 to cell 7	38. N-5 to cell 3
8. N-6 to cell 3	24. N-4 to cell 9	39. N-2 to cell 9
9. N-3 to cell 9	25. N-1 to cell 11	40. P-5 to cell 12
10. N-2 to cell 15	26. P-8 to cell 17	41. P-4 to cell 12
11. P-8 to cell 16	27. P-7 to cell 16	42. N-2 to cell 6
12. P-7 to cell 10	28. N-5 to cell 10	43. N-1 to cell 9
13. N-3 to cell 8	29. P-3 to cell 13	44. P-5 to cell 11
14. N-7 to cell 9	30. P-5 to cell 12	45. P-1 to cell 10
15. N-4 to cell 11	31. P-4 to cell 6	46. N-1 to cell 8
16. P-6 to cell 14		

Thirty-six

Twelve is the greatest number: i.e. on squares 4A, 6A, 2B, 4B, 5C, 6C, D1, D2, E3, E5, F1, F3.

Twenty-five

1.	Move 5 over 8, 9, 3, 1	3. Move 6 over 2 and 7
2.	Move 7 over 4.	4. Move 5 over 6

Sixteen

Transfer a coin from square 8 to square 10, then play as follows, always removing the coin jumped over.

1. 9 to 11	4. 16 to 8	7. 3 to 1
2. 1 to 9	5. 4 to 12	8. 1 to 9
3. 13 to 5	6. 12 to 10	9. 9 to 11

Three Piles

(a) Move seven matches from pile 1 to pile 2
(b) Move 6 matches from pile 2 to pile 3
(c) Move 4 matches from pile 3 to pile 1

The Twelve-Match Challenge

1.

2.

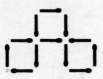

3.

4.

5.

6.

7.

Two Dozen Matches

1.

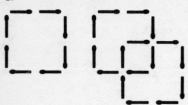

5.

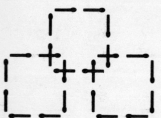

2.

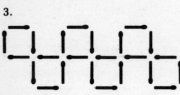

6.

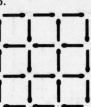

3.

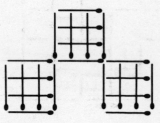

7.

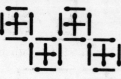

4.

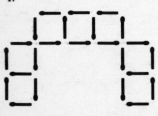

8.

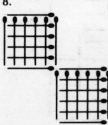

The Farmer's Children

With the land divided equally between six:

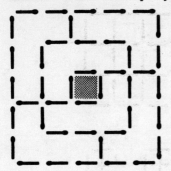

And the land divided equally between eight:

The Brown Boys

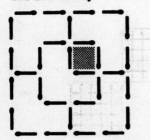

Terrific Triangles

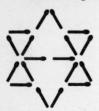

Terrifying Triangles

Triangular

Squarely Triangular

Triangularly Triangular
(Yes, it's three-dimensional!)

Small Squares

Six out of Nine

Three out of Five

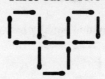

Three out of Six

Roman Puzzles

1. $III + II = V$

2. $IV + I = V$

3. $V + IV = IX$

   $VI + IV = X$

4. $VII - V = II$

5. $II - I = I$

6. All you need to do is walk round to the other side of the table and the sum makes sense!

The Climbing Frame

The Six Containers

All Square

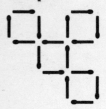

Long Division

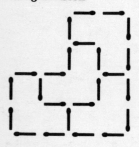

Amazing

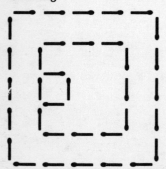

Elevenses

Ten

Nine

All You Need

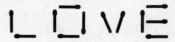

SHAPES AND SIZES

Tangram

The Rectangle

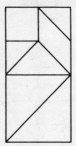

The Triangle

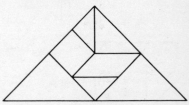

The Parallelogram

The Hollow Parallelogram

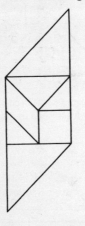

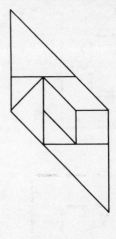

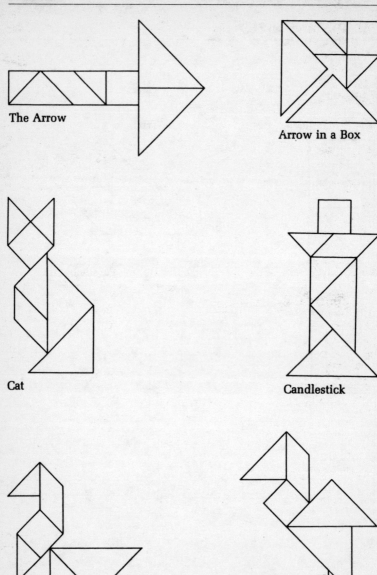

The Arrow

Arrow in a Box

Cat

Candlestick

Swan

Heron

Horse and Rider

Sailing Boat

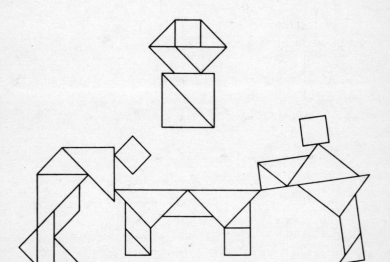

A Game of Billiards

Cinderella

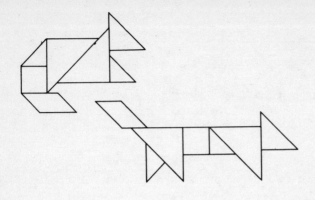

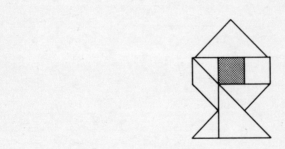

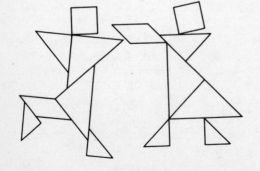

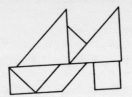

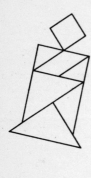

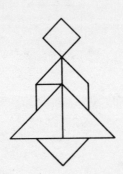

Octogram

The Birds

The Cats

The Heart of the Matter

Multi-Shapes

1. Four

2. Nine

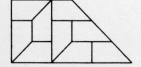

3. **Sixteen**

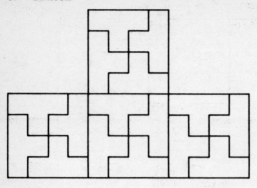

All Square

1. **Triangular Square**

2. **Cross Square**

3. A Rectangular Square

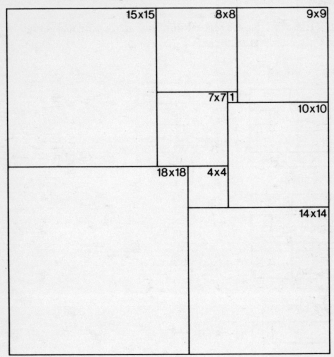

4. Unsquare

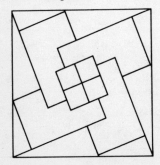

This only works because it doesn't! Neither of the figures is really a square: one is slightly longer at the edges and one slightly narrower.

Pentominoes

For some of these challenges several solutions are possible, although in each case only one is given here.

1. **Three by Five**

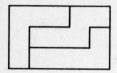

2. **Four by Five**

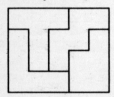

3. **Five by Five**

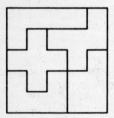

4. **Five by Six**

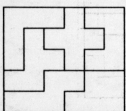

5.   **Five by Seven**

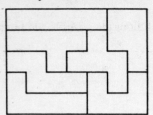

6.   **Four by Ten**

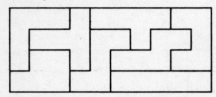

7.   **Six by Ten**

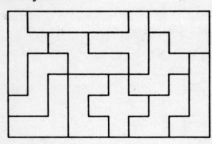

8.   **Five by Twelve**

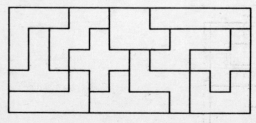

9. **Four by Fifteen**

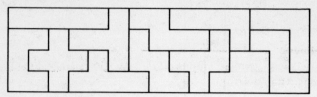

10. **Square with Hole**

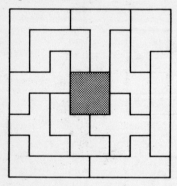

11. **Square without Corners**

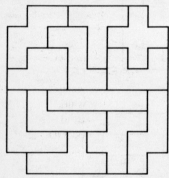

PENCIL AND PAPER GAMES

Changelings
These are Lewis Carroll's solutions. You may have managed the transformations with fewer links.

1. PIG
   wig
   wag
   way
   say
   STY

2. FOUR
   foul
   fool
   foot
   fort
   fore
   fire
   FIVE

3. WHEAT
   cheat
   cheap
   cheep
   creep
   creed
   breed
   BREAD

4. NOSE
   note
   cote
   core
   corn
   coin
   CHIN

5. TEARS
   sears
   stars
   stare
   stale
   stile
   SMILE

6. HARE
   hark
   hack
   sack
   sock
   soak
   soap
   SOUP

7. PITCH
   pinch
   winch
   wench
   tench
   tenth
   TENTS

8. EYE
   dye
   die
   did
   LID

9. PITY
   pits
   pins
   fins
   find
   fond
   food
   GOOD

10. POOR
    boor
    book
    rook
    rock
    rick
    RICH

11. TREE
    free
    flee
    fled
    feed
    weed
    weld
    wold
    WOOD

12. GRASS
    crass
    cress
    tress
    trees
    frees
    freed
    greed
    GREEN

13. APE
    are
    ere
    err
    ear
    mar
    MAN

14. FLOUR
    floor
    flood
    blood
    brood
    broad
    BREAD

15. ELM
    ell
    all
    ail
    air
    fir
    far
    oar
    OAK

16. TEA
    sea
    set
    sot
    HOT

17. MINE
    mint
    mist
    most
    moat
    coat
    COAL

18. BLACK
    blank
    blink
    clink
    chink
    chine
    whine
    WHITE

19. WITCH
    winch
    wench
    tench
    tenth
    tents
    tints
    tilts
    tills
    fills
    falls
    fails
    fairs
    FAIRY

20. WINTER
    winner
    wanner
    wander
    warder
    harder
    harper
    hamper
    damper
    damped
    dimmed
    dimmer
    simmer
    SUMMER

Odd Man Out
Always start from the circle that is two away from the circle you started
with previously. In other words you should put the next dot in the circle
you previously started from.

Pencil Power
1. Take the following route: E–B–D–C–B–A–C–F–D–E–F.
2. Start with C and take the following route: C–D–J–F–H–J–K–E–F–
    B–E–A–C–F.

3.   Take the following route: A to B; by upper curve to E; to D; by upper
     curve to C; straighten line to D; by lower curve to C; straight line to B;
     by lower curve to E; to F.

Pen Power
Draw a large pen and then draw three small pens inside it. Now put three
pigs in each of the three pens and you will have an odd number of pigs in
each of the four pens and the large pen will have nine pigs in it.

Round Numbers

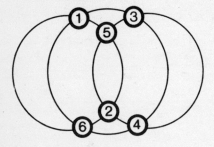

MENTAL GAMES

Pick a Number
1. 301
2. 2519
3. 13,458 is twice 6,729
4. 6 and 10, 4 and 3, 1 and 5, 8 and 9, 2 and 7
5. 4368
6. 219; 438, and 657
7. 8, 12, 5 and 20. $8 + 2 = 10$; $12 - 2 = 10$; $5 \times 2 = 10$;
   $20 \div 2 = 10$.
8. 12. $(12 - 7)5 = (12 - 5)7 = 35$.
9. 1, 2, 4, 7 and 14 make a total of 28.
10. ⅔ and ⅓
11. The father is 40, the son 10.

12. The father is 73, the son 37
13. The man is 52, his wife 39
14. Three pounds.
15. 17 beasts and 26 birds.
16. 3 girls and 4 boys
17. Each increase saves one minute per mile. From 30 miles an hour you would have to increase your speed to 60 in order to save a minute per mile. At 60 miles an hour, it is impossible.
18. 300 miles.
19. 26⅔ miles an hour
20. Five cats.

1	14	7	12
15	4	9	6
10	5	16	3
8	11	2	13

Word Power

1. a leaf
2. a peace proposal
3. a wind
4. a tree
5. a Neapolitan beggar
6. a wild ass
7. a novice
8. a Turkish bath
9. a bird of prey
10. a measure of weight
11. an ox
12. a kind of rum
13. a poisonous drug
14. a herb
15. a stalk
16. a tea
17. somebody with whom pawn is deposited
18. a kind of gout
19. a pagan

CHILDREN'S GAMES

Mirror Images
(a) C   D   E   H   I   O   X
(b) A   H   I   M   O   T   V   W   X
(c) H   I   O   X
The word is: OXO

Mental Pictures
1. Against the palm.
2. From the top right-hand corner to the bottom left.
3. Two.
4. Outside at the front.

Paper and Pencil Challenge
1. Give one end of the strip just half a turn before joining the ends so that the ring has a slight twist in it. When you draw your line on it the paper will seem to have one side only.
2. Join these letters: PLFBHDJNTXRVP
3. 4 9 2
   3 5 7
   8 1 6

Twenty Questions
1. P G T W. The letters are the initials of the first four lines of the old song *Pop Goes the Weasel*.
2. 24, 20, 16, 12.
3. S is the letter. Scythe and Chesty are the words.
4. Tom will get 2,500; Dick 1,500, and Harry 700.
5. Farmer Giles had 49 acres and Farmer Brown had 35 acres.
6. £10,737,418 and 24 pence!
7. Six dozen dozen is $6 \times 12 \times 12 = 864$; a half dozen dozen is simply $6 \times 12 = 72$. The difference between the two figures is 792.
8. The word is 'herein' and the words inside it are 'he', 'her', 'here', 'ere', 'rein', and 'in'.
9. SOMERSAULT.
10. Just one word.
11. 300 miles.

12. Three.
13. In each one of them are three letters in their normal alphabetical order: LMN, NOP, DEF, RST, GHI, and STU.
14. Uncomplimentary.
15. 4 years ago.
16. The letters are the first two letters of each of the months of the year.
17. Four.
18. 9.30.
19. One.
20. GYLES BRANDRETH.

INDEX

The titles of chapters are given in capitals.